SRa SPECTRUM MATH

brown

FOURTH EDITION

AUTHORS
Thomas J. Richards
Mathematics Teacher
Lamar Middle School
Lamar, Missouri

Marjorie Diggs Freeman
Mathematics Enrichment Program
Southwest Elementary School
Durham, North Carolina

SRA/McGraw-Hill
Columbus, Ohio

SRA/McGraw-Hill

A Division of The McGraw·Hill Companies

Send all inquiries to:
SRA/McGraw-Hill
250 Old Wilson Bridge Road
Suite 310
Worthington, OH 43085

Printed in the United States of America.

ISBN 0-02-687542-X

2 3 4 5 POH 00 99 98 97

Contents

Chapter 7
Numeration, Addition, and Subtraction
(3-digit; no renaming)

Lesson 1   Numbers 0 Through 10

Write the numeral for each number.

three ★ ★ ★ **3**___   one ⬤ ____

five ⬤ ⬤ ⬤ ⬤ ⬤ ____   zero ____

two ✏ ✏ ____   six ❘❘❘❘❘❘____

eight ⬤ ⬤ ⬤ ⬤ ⬤ ⬤ ⬤ ⬤ ____

ten △ △ △ △ △ △ △ △ △ △ ____

nine ⬡ ⬡ ⬡ ⬡ ⬡ ⬡ ⬡ ⬡ ⬡ ____

seven ♥ ♥ ♥ ♥ ♥ ♥ ♥ ____

four ◻ ◻ ◻ ◻ ____

Tell how many dots.

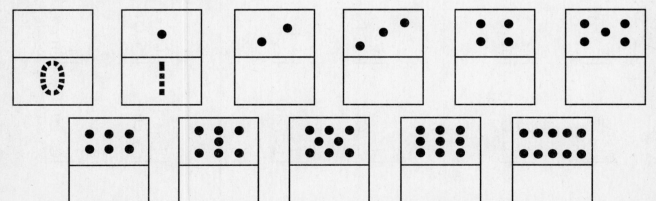

Lesson 2 Facts Through 5

Add or subtract.

□ □   □

$$\begin{array}{r} 1 \\ +1 \\ \hline \mathbf{2} \end{array}$$ $$\begin{array}{r} 2 \\ -1 \\ \hline \mathbf{1} \end{array}$$

□ □ □   □ □   □ □ □

$$\begin{array}{r} 2 \\ +1 \\ \hline \end{array}$$ $$\begin{array}{r} 1 \\ +2 \\ \hline \end{array}$$ $$\begin{array}{r} 3 \\ -1 \\ \hline \end{array}$$ $$\begin{array}{r} 3 \\ -2 \\ \hline \end{array}$$

□ □ □ □

$$\begin{array}{r} 3 \\ +1 \\ \hline \end{array}$$ $$\begin{array}{r} 1 \\ +3 \\ \hline \end{array}$$

$$\begin{array}{r} 4 \\ -1 \\ \hline \end{array}$$ $$\begin{array}{r} 4 \\ -3 \\ \hline \end{array}$$

□ □ □ □

$$\begin{array}{r} 2 \\ +2 \\ \hline \end{array}$$

$$\begin{array}{r} 4 \\ -2 \\ \hline \end{array}$$

□ □ □ □

$$\begin{array}{r} 4 \\ +0 \\ \hline \end{array}$$ $$\begin{array}{r} 0 \\ +4 \\ \hline \end{array}$$

$$\begin{array}{r} 4 \\ -0 \\ \hline \end{array}$$ $$\begin{array}{r} 4 \\ -4 \\ \hline \end{array}$$

□ □ □ □ □

$$\begin{array}{r} 3 \\ +2 \\ \hline \end{array}$$ $$\begin{array}{r} 2 \\ +3 \\ \hline \end{array}$$

$$\begin{array}{r} 5 \\ -2 \\ \hline \end{array}$$ $$\begin{array}{r} 5 \\ -3 \\ \hline \end{array}$$

□ □ □ □ □

$$\begin{array}{r} 4 \\ +1 \\ \hline \end{array}$$ $$\begin{array}{r} 1 \\ +4 \\ \hline \end{array}$$

$$\begin{array}{r} 5 \\ -1 \\ \hline \end{array}$$ $$\begin{array}{r} 5 \\ -4 \\ \hline \end{array}$$

□ □ □ □ □

$$\begin{array}{r} 5 \\ +0 \\ \hline \end{array}$$ $$\begin{array}{r} 0 \\ +5 \\ \hline \end{array}$$

$$\begin{array}{r} 5 \\ -0 \\ \hline \end{array}$$ $$\begin{array}{r} 5 \\ -5 \\ \hline \end{array}$$

Lesson 3 Facts for 6 and 7

Add or subtract.

5	1	6	6
+1	+5	−1	−5
6		**5**	

3	6		4	2	6	6
+3	−3		+2	+4	−2	−4

4	3		5	2		6	1
+3	+4		+2	+5		+1	+6

7	7		7	7		7	7
−3	−4		−2	−5		−1	−6

3	5	6		7	7	6
+3	+2	+0		−7	−4	−2

Lesson 4   Facts for 8

Add or subtract.

$$\begin{array}{cc} 5 & 3 \\ +3 & +5 \\ \hline \end{array}$$

8

$$\begin{array}{c} 8 \\ -3 \\ \hline \end{array}$$

5

$$\begin{array}{c} 8 \\ -5 \\ \hline \end{array}$$

$$\begin{array}{c} 4 \\ +4 \\ \hline \end{array}$$

$$\begin{array}{cc} 6 & 2 \\ +2 & +6 \\ \hline \end{array}$$

$$\begin{array}{cc} 7 & 1 \\ +1 & +7 \\ \hline \end{array}$$

$$\begin{array}{c} 8 \\ -4 \\ \hline \end{array}$$

$$\begin{array}{cc} 8 & 8 \\ -2 & -6 \\ \hline \end{array}$$

$$\begin{array}{cc} 8 & 8 \\ -1 & -7 \\ \hline \end{array}$$

$$\begin{array}{cccccc} 2 & 4 & 5 & 3 & 7 & 0 \\ +6 & +3 & +1 & +5 & +1 & +8 \\ \hline \end{array}$$

$$\begin{array}{cccccc} 8 & 7 & 8 & 6 & 8 & 8 \\ -1 & -6 & -5 & -3 & -0 & -2 \\ \hline \end{array}$$

Lesson 5   Facts for 9

Add or subtract.

$$\begin{array}{r} 5 \\ +4 \\ \hline 9 \end{array} \qquad \begin{array}{r} 4 \\ +5 \\ \hline \end{array}$$

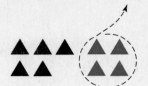

$$\begin{array}{r} 9 \\ -4 \\ \hline 5 \end{array}$$

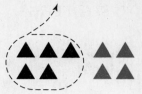

$$\begin{array}{r} 9 \\ -5 \\ \hline \end{array}$$

$$\begin{array}{r} 6 \\ +3 \\ \hline \end{array} \qquad \begin{array}{r} 3 \\ +6 \\ \hline \end{array}$$

$$\begin{array}{r} 7 \\ +2 \\ \hline \end{array} \qquad \begin{array}{r} 2 \\ +7 \\ \hline \end{array}$$

$$\begin{array}{r} 8 \\ +1 \\ \hline \end{array} \qquad \begin{array}{r} 1 \\ +8 \\ \hline \end{array}$$

$$\begin{array}{r} 9 \\ -3 \\ \hline \end{array} \qquad \begin{array}{r} 9 \\ -6 \\ \hline \end{array}$$

$$\begin{array}{r} 9 \\ -2 \\ \hline \end{array} \qquad \begin{array}{r} 9 \\ -7 \\ \hline \end{array}$$

$$\begin{array}{r} 9 \\ -1 \\ \hline \end{array} \qquad \begin{array}{r} 9 \\ -8 \\ \hline \end{array}$$

$$\begin{array}{r} 5 \\ +4 \\ \hline \end{array} \qquad \begin{array}{r} 2 \\ +7 \\ \hline \end{array} \qquad \begin{array}{r} 6 \\ +1 \\ \hline \end{array} \qquad \begin{array}{r} 9 \\ +0 \\ \hline \end{array} \qquad \begin{array}{r} 1 \\ +8 \\ \hline \end{array} \qquad \begin{array}{r} 4 \\ +4 \\ \hline \end{array}$$

$$\begin{array}{r} 9 \\ -5 \\ \hline \end{array} \qquad \begin{array}{r} 7 \\ -3 \\ \hline \end{array} \qquad \begin{array}{r} 9 \\ -8 \\ \hline \end{array} \qquad \begin{array}{r} 9 \\ -3 \\ \hline \end{array} \qquad \begin{array}{r} 9 \\ -9 \\ \hline \end{array} \qquad \begin{array}{r} 9 \\ -0 \\ \hline \end{array}$$

Lesson 6 Facts for 10

Add or subtract.

$$\begin{array}{r} 5 \\ +5 \\ \hline 10 \end{array}$$

$$\begin{array}{r} 10 \\ -5 \\ \hline 5 \end{array}$$

$$\begin{array}{r} 6 \\ +4 \\ \hline \end{array} \qquad \begin{array}{r} 4 \\ +6 \\ \hline \end{array}$$

$$\begin{array}{r} 10 \\ -4 \\ \hline \end{array} \qquad \begin{array}{r} 10 \\ -6 \\ \hline \end{array}$$

$$\begin{array}{r} 7 \\ +3 \\ \hline \end{array} \qquad \begin{array}{r} 3 \\ +7 \\ \hline \end{array}$$

$$\begin{array}{r} 10 \\ -3 \\ \hline \end{array} \qquad \begin{array}{r} 10 \\ -7 \\ \hline \end{array}$$

$$\begin{array}{r} 8 \\ +2 \\ \hline \end{array} \qquad \begin{array}{r} 2 \\ +8 \\ \hline \end{array}$$

$$\begin{array}{r} 10 \\ -2 \\ \hline \end{array} \qquad \begin{array}{r} 10 \\ -8 \\ \hline \end{array}$$

$$\begin{array}{r} 9 \\ +1 \\ \hline \end{array} \qquad \begin{array}{r} 1 \\ +9 \\ \hline \end{array}$$

$$\begin{array}{r} 10 \\ -1 \\ \hline \end{array} \qquad \begin{array}{r} 10 \\ -9 \\ \hline \end{array}$$

$$\begin{array}{r} 4 \\ +6 \\ \hline \end{array} \qquad \begin{array}{r} 5 \\ +5 \\ \hline \end{array} \qquad \begin{array}{r} 9 \\ +1 \\ \hline \end{array} \qquad \begin{array}{r} 10 \\ -8 \\ \hline \end{array} \qquad \begin{array}{r} 10 \\ -3 \\ \hline \end{array} \qquad \begin{array}{r} 10 \\ -0 \\ \hline \end{array}$$

Lesson 7 Facts Through 10

Add.

5 +4 **9**	4 +3	1 +2	5 +3	4 +6	4 +4
0 +6	4 +1	8 +1	9 +1	8 +2	2 +2
2 +7	5 +2	1 +6	5 +5	4 +5	6 +2

Subtract.

10 −6 **4**	8 −2	5 −3	7 −6	4 −3	10 −5
9 −3	10 −2	7 −2	8 −6	10 −9	8 −8
10 −4	9 −6	9 −8	8 −1	10 −7	7 −4

Solve each problem.

$$
\begin{array}{r}
4 \\
+\ 3 \\
\hline
7
\end{array}
$$

leaves on the ground

leaves falling

leaves in all

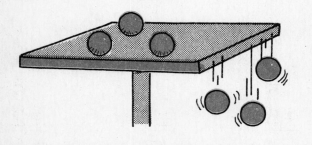

$$
\begin{array}{r}
\\
-\ \\
\hline
\\
\end{array}
$$

balls in all

balls falling

balls not falling

$$
\begin{array}{r}
\\
+\ \\
\hline
\\
\end{array}
$$

fish by a rock

more fish coming

fish in all

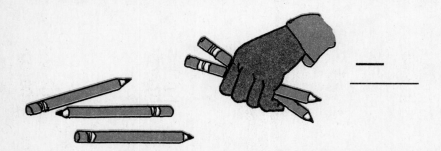

$$
\begin{array}{r}
\\
-\ \\
\hline
\\
\end{array}
$$

pencils in all

pencils taken

pencils not taken

$$
\begin{array}{r}
\\
+\ \\
\hline
\\
\end{array}
$$

puppies on a rug

more puppies coming

puppies in all

CHAPTER 1   CHECKUP

Add.

2 +4	7 +3	4 +5	6 +2	2 +3	0 +4
4 +3	1 +5	2 +8	3 +3	6 +4	2 +1
3 +1	7 +0	8 +1	5 +2	3 +6	5 +5

Subtract.

3 −3	5 −2	10 −6	9 −2	7 −3	10 −5
9 −1	8 −7	1 −0	6 −4	8 −5	10 −8
9 −6	4 −3	6 −3	7 −5	10 −9	8 −4

Tell how many.

 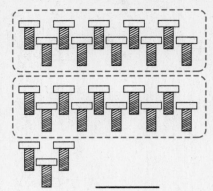 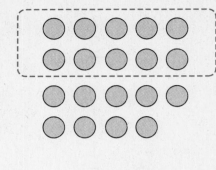

_____   _____   _____

Complete.

1 ten 3 ones = _____   2 tens = _____

3 tens 4 ones = _____   4 tens 6 ones = _____

8 tens = _____   7 tens 9 ones = _____

Write the next four numbers.

6, 7, 8, _____, _____, _____, _____

24, 25, 26, _____, _____, _____, _____

50, 51, 52, _____, _____, _____, _____

67, 68, 69, _____, _____, _____, _____

Lesson 1 Numbers 11 Through 18

1¢   10¢   10¢

Complete.

      _____ ten _____ one = _____

    _____ ten _____ ones = _____

    _____ ten _____ ones = _____

    _____ ten _____ ones = _____

    _____ ten _____ ones = _____

    _____ ten _____ ones = _____

    _____ ten _____ ones = _____

    _____ ten _____ ones = _____

Lesson 2   Numbers 19 Through 39
Complete.

___2___ tens = ___20___

_____ tens _____ ones = _____

_____ ten _____ ones = _____

_____ tens _____ ones = _____

_____ tens = _____

_____ tens _____ ones = _____

_____ tens _____ ones = _____

_____ tens _____ ones = _____

Lesson 3   Numbers 40 Through 99

Complete.

_**4**_ tens = _**40**_

____ tens ____ ones = ____

____ tens ____ ones = ____

____ tens ____ ones = ____

____ tens = ____

____ tens ____ ones = ____

____ tens ____ ones = ____

____ tens ____ ones = ____

Complete.

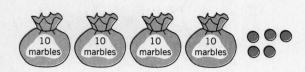

___4___ tens ___5___ ones = ___45___

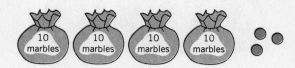

_____ tens _____ ones = _____

_____ tens = _____

_____ tens _____ ones = _____

_____ tens _____ ones = _____

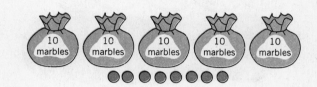

_____ tens _____ ones = _____

_____ tens = _____

_____ tens = _____

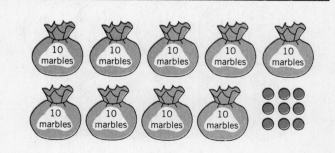

_____ tens _____ ones = _____

Lesson 4   Numbers Through 99
Complete.

4 tens 6 ones = **46**

1 ten 2 ones = _____

3 tens 7 ones = _____

2 tens 4 ones = _____

9 tens = _____

6 tens = _____

5 tens 3 ones = _____

7 tens 8 ones = _____

1 ten 1 one = _____

8 tens 4 ones = _____

3 tens 5 ones = _____

4 tens 9 ones = _____

9 tens 6 ones = _____

2 tens 1 one = _____

5 tens 7 ones = _____

1 ten 9 ones = _____

8 tens 8 ones = _____

6 tens 7 ones = _____

7 tens 2 ones = _____

9 tens 5 ones = _____

4 tens 1 one = _____

3 tens 4 ones = _____

6 tens 6 ones = _____

8 tens 9 ones = _____

2 tens = _____

5 tens = _____

NAME _____

Write numbers in order.

0	1								
10					15				
									29
			33						
40							47		
			54						

Connect the dots in order.

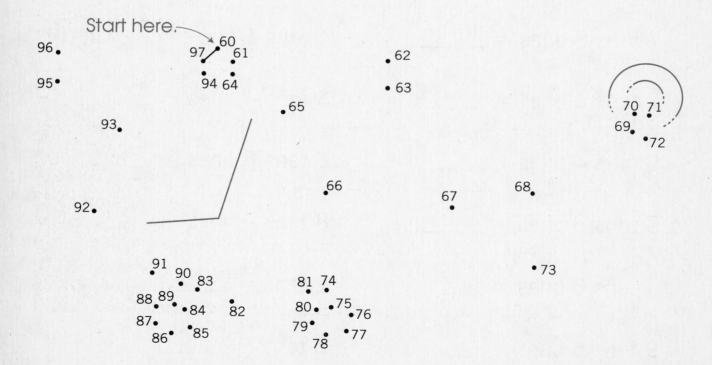

Lesson 5   Numbers Through 99

Write the next four numbers.

6, 7, 8, __9__ , __10__ , __11__ , __12__

22, 23, 24, ____ , ____ , ____ , ____

37, 38, 39, ____ , ____ , ____ , ____

15, 16, 17, ____ , ____ , ____ , ____

51, 52, 53, ____ , ____ , ____ , ____

44, 45, 46, ____ , ____ , ____ , ____

76, 77, 78, ____ , ____ , ____ , ____

82, 83, 84, ____ , ____ , ____ , ____

68, 69, 70, ____ , ____ , ____ , ____

86, 87, 88, ____ , ____ , ____ , ____

55, 56, 57, ____ , ____ , ____ , ____

93, 94, 95, ____ , ____ , ____ , ____

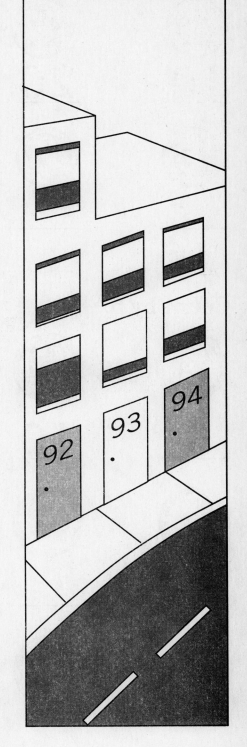

Lesson 6 Skip Counting

Count by 10.

__10__ , __20__ , __30__ , _____ , _____ ,

_____ , _____ , _____ , _____

Count by 5.

__5__ , __10__ , __15__ , _____ , _____ ,

_____ , _____ , _____ , _____ , _____ ,

_____ , _____ , _____ , _____ ,

CHAPTER 2   CHECKUP

Complete.

2 tens 8 ones = _____   5 tens = _____

3 tens 1 one = _____   4 tens 5 ones = _____

7 tens = _____   8 tens 2 ones = _____

6 tens 6 ones = _____   9 tens 8 ones = _____

9 tens = _____   7 tens 9 ones = _____

Write the next four numbers.

4, 5, 6, _____, _____, _____, _____

37, 38, 39, _____, _____, _____, _____

53, 54, 55, _____, _____, _____, _____

61, 62, 63, _____, _____, _____, _____

78, 79, 80, _____, _____, _____, _____

86, 87, 88, _____, _____, _____, _____

PRE-TEST

Add.

3	5	2	7	4	6
+4	+4	+8	+2	+6	+2

5	3	9	6	8	2
+7	+8	+4	+6	+5	+9

7	9	8	4	8	6
+7	+6	+7	+9	+8	+8

Subtract.

6	5	9	8	10	7
−3	−4	−7	−2	− 7	−0

11	13	11	12	13	12
− 7	− 6	− 5	− 4	− 4	− 9

14	17	16	14	15	18
− 5	− 9	− 7	− 7	− 6	− 9

Lesson 1 Addition Facts Through 12

Add.

$$\begin{array}{r} 2 \\ +9 \\ \hline \end{array}$$
11

$$\begin{array}{r} 9 \\ +2 \\ \hline \end{array}$$

$$\begin{array}{r} 3 \\ +8 \\ \hline \end{array}$$

$$\begin{array}{r} 8 \\ +3 \\ \hline \end{array}$$

$$\begin{array}{r} 5 \\ +6 \\ \hline \end{array}$$

$$\begin{array}{r} 6 \\ +5 \\ \hline \end{array}$$

$$\begin{array}{r} 4 \\ +7 \\ \hline \end{array}$$

$$\begin{array}{r} 7 \\ +4 \\ \hline \end{array}$$

$$\begin{array}{r} 8 \\ +4 \\ \hline \end{array}$$

$$\begin{array}{r} 4 \\ +8 \\ \hline \end{array}$$

$$\begin{array}{r} 7 \\ +5 \\ \hline \end{array}$$

$$\begin{array}{r} 5 \\ +7 \\ \hline \end{array}$$

$$\begin{array}{r} 9 \\ +3 \\ \hline \end{array}$$

$$\begin{array}{r} 3 \\ +9 \\ \hline \end{array}$$

$$\begin{array}{r} 6 \\ +6 \\ \hline \end{array}$$

Add.

$$\begin{array}{r} 8 \\ +3 \\ \hline \end{array}$$

$$\begin{array}{r} 6 \\ +6 \\ \hline \end{array}$$

$$\begin{array}{r} 9 \\ +3 \\ \hline \end{array}$$

$$\begin{array}{r} 3 \\ +8 \\ \hline \end{array}$$

$$\begin{array}{r} 4 \\ +7 \\ \hline \end{array}$$

$$\begin{array}{r} 2 \\ +9 \\ \hline \end{array}$$

$$\begin{array}{r} 5 \\ +7 \\ \hline \end{array}$$

$$\begin{array}{r} 8 \\ +4 \\ \hline \end{array}$$

$$\begin{array}{r} 7 \\ +5 \\ \hline \end{array}$$

$$\begin{array}{r} 5 \\ +6 \\ \hline \end{array}$$

$$\begin{array}{r} 9 \\ +2 \\ \hline \end{array}$$

$$\begin{array}{r} 4 \\ +8 \\ \hline \end{array}$$

Solve each problem.

 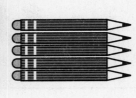

6   pencils in a box

+5   more pencils

_____ pencils in all

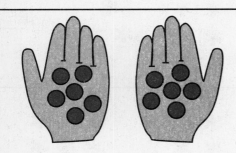

_____ grapes on a plate

_____ more grapes

_____ grapes in all

_____ marbles in one hand

_____ marbles in the other hand

_____ marbles in all

_____ people at the table

_____ more people coming in

_____ people in all

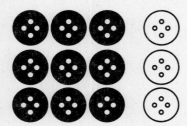

_____ black buttons

_____ white buttons

_____ buttons in all

SPECTRUM MATHEMATICS,
Brown Book

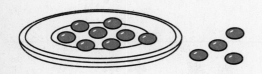

Lesson 2 Subtraction Facts Through 12

Subtract.

$$\begin{array}{r} 11 \\ -9 \\ \hline \end{array}$$
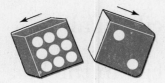
$$\begin{array}{r} 11 \\ -2 \\ \hline \end{array}$$
$$\begin{array}{r} 11 \\ -8 \\ \hline \end{array}$$
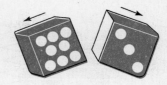
$$\begin{array}{r} 11 \\ -3 \\ \hline \end{array}$$

$$\begin{array}{r} 11 \\ -6 \\ \hline \end{array}$$

$$\begin{array}{r} 11 \\ -5 \\ \hline \end{array}$$
$$\begin{array}{r} 11 \\ -7 \\ \hline \end{array}$$

$$\begin{array}{r} 11 \\ -4 \\ \hline \end{array}$$

$$\begin{array}{r} 12 \\ -8 \\ \hline \end{array}$$
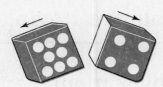
$$\begin{array}{r} 12 \\ -4 \\ \hline \end{array}$$
$$\begin{array}{r} 12 \\ -7 \\ \hline \end{array}$$

$$\begin{array}{r} 12 \\ -5 \\ \hline \end{array}$$

$$\begin{array}{r} 12 \\ -9 \\ \hline \end{array}$$
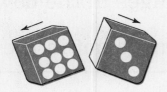
$$\begin{array}{r} 12 \\ -3 \\ \hline \end{array}$$
$$\begin{array}{r} 12 \\ -6 \\ \hline \end{array}$$

Subtract.

$$\begin{array}{r} 11 \\ -3 \\ \hline \end{array}$$
$$\begin{array}{r} 11 \\ -6 \\ \hline \end{array}$$
$$\begin{array}{r} 12 \\ -3 \\ \hline \end{array}$$
$$\begin{array}{r} 11 \\ -8 \\ \hline \end{array}$$
$$\begin{array}{r} 12 \\ -7 \\ \hline \end{array}$$
$$\begin{array}{r} 12 \\ -9 \\ \hline \end{array}$$

$$\begin{array}{r} 11 \\ -7 \\ \hline \end{array}$$
$$\begin{array}{r} 12 \\ -4 \\ \hline \end{array}$$
$$\begin{array}{r} 12 \\ -5 \\ \hline \end{array}$$
$$\begin{array}{r} 12 \\ -6 \\ \hline \end{array}$$
$$\begin{array}{r} 11 \\ -2 \\ \hline \end{array}$$
$$\begin{array}{r} 12 \\ -8 \\ \hline \end{array}$$

Solve each problem.

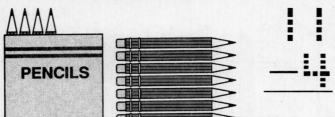

_____ pencils in all

_____ pencils in the box

_____ pencils not in the box

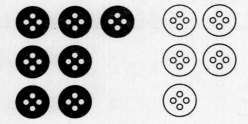

_____ people in all

_____ people are leaving

_____ people are staying

_____ oranges in all

_____ oranges in the bowl

_____ oranges not in the bowl

_____ buttons in all

_____ black buttons

_____ white buttons

_____ candles in all

_____ candles lit

_____ candles not lit

Lesson 3   Addition Facts Through 14

Add.

$$\begin{array}{r} 6 \\ +7 \\ \hline 13 \end{array}$$

$$\begin{array}{r} 7 \\ +6 \\ \hline \end{array}$$

$$\begin{array}{r} 5 \\ +8 \\ \hline \end{array}$$

$$\begin{array}{r} 8 \\ +5 \\ \hline \end{array}$$

$$\begin{array}{r} 9 \\ +4 \\ \hline \end{array}$$

$$\begin{array}{r} 4 \\ +9 \\ \hline \end{array}$$

$$\begin{array}{r} 9 \\ +5 \\ \hline \end{array}$$

$$\begin{array}{r} 5 \\ +9 \\ \hline \end{array}$$

$$\begin{array}{r} 8 \\ +6 \\ \hline \end{array}$$

$$\begin{array}{r} 6 \\ +8 \\ \hline \end{array}$$

$$\begin{array}{r} 7 \\ +7 \\ \hline \end{array}$$

Add.

$$\begin{array}{r} 7 \\ +7 \\ \hline \end{array} \qquad \begin{array}{r} 5 \\ +8 \\ \hline \end{array} \qquad \begin{array}{r} 9 \\ +4 \\ \hline \end{array} \qquad \begin{array}{r} 8 \\ +6 \\ \hline \end{array} \qquad \begin{array}{r} 4 \\ +9 \\ \hline \end{array} \qquad \begin{array}{r} 5 \\ +9 \\ \hline \end{array}$$

$$\begin{array}{r} 8 \\ +5 \\ \hline \end{array} \qquad \begin{array}{r} 6 \\ +8 \\ \hline \end{array} \qquad \begin{array}{r} 9 \\ +5 \\ \hline \end{array} \qquad \begin{array}{r} 6 \\ +6 \\ \hline \end{array} \qquad \begin{array}{r} 7 \\ +6 \\ \hline \end{array} \qquad \begin{array}{r} 6 \\ +7 \\ \hline \end{array}$$

Lesson 4   Subtraction Facts Through 14

NAME _____

Subtract.

$$\begin{array}{r} 13 \\ -5 \\ \hline 8 \end{array}$$

$$\begin{array}{r} 14 \\ -9 \\ \hline \end{array}$$

$$\begin{array}{r} 14 \\ -8 \\ \hline \end{array}$$

$$\begin{array}{r} 13 \\ -4 \\ \hline \end{array}$$

$$\begin{array}{r} 13 \\ -6 \\ \hline \end{array}$$

$$\begin{array}{r} 14 \\ -5 \\ \hline \end{array}$$

Subtract.

$$\begin{array}{r} 12 \\ -7 \\ \hline 5 \end{array}$$
$$\begin{array}{r} 10 \\ -2 \\ \hline \end{array}$$
$$\begin{array}{r} 13 \\ -4 \\ \hline \end{array}$$
$$\begin{array}{r} 14 \\ -9 \\ \hline \end{array}$$
$$\begin{array}{r} 11 \\ -8 \\ \hline \end{array}$$
$$\begin{array}{r} 14 \\ -5 \\ \hline \end{array}$$

$$\begin{array}{r} 14 \\ -6 \\ \hline \end{array}$$
$$\begin{array}{r} 12 \\ -8 \\ \hline \end{array}$$
$$\begin{array}{r} 13 \\ -5 \\ \hline \end{array}$$
$$\begin{array}{r} 10 \\ -6 \\ \hline \end{array}$$
$$\begin{array}{r} 13 \\ -6 \\ \hline \end{array}$$
$$\begin{array}{r} 13 \\ -7 \\ \hline \end{array}$$

$$\begin{array}{r} 11 \\ -6 \\ \hline \end{array}$$
$$\begin{array}{r} 13 \\ -9 \\ \hline \end{array}$$
$$\begin{array}{r} 14 \\ -8 \\ \hline \end{array}$$
$$\begin{array}{r} 12 \\ -3 \\ \hline \end{array}$$
$$\begin{array}{r} 14 \\ -7 \\ \hline \end{array}$$
$$\begin{array}{r} 13 \\ -8 \\ \hline \end{array}$$

Lesson 5 Addition Facts Through 18

Add.

$\begin{array}{r}6\\+9\\\hline 15\end{array}$ 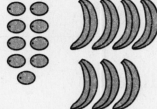 $\begin{array}{r}9\\+6\\\hline\end{array}$ | $\begin{array}{r}8\\+7\\\hline\end{array}$ 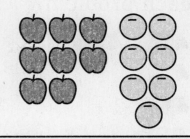 $\begin{array}{r}7\\+8\\\hline\end{array}$

$\begin{array}{r}9\\+7\\\hline\end{array}$ 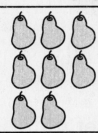 $\begin{array}{r}7\\+9\\\hline\end{array}$ | $\begin{array}{r}8\\+9\\\hline\end{array}$  $\begin{array}{r}9\\+8\\\hline\end{array}$

$\begin{array}{r}8\\+8\\\hline\end{array}$  | $\begin{array}{r}9\\+9\\\hline\end{array}$

Add.

| $\begin{array}{r}9\\+6\\\hline 15\end{array}$ | $\begin{array}{r}7\\+8\\\hline\end{array}$ | $\begin{array}{r}9\\+9\\\hline\end{array}$ | $\begin{array}{r}7\\+9\\\hline\end{array}$ | $\begin{array}{r}8\\+9\\\hline\end{array}$ | $\begin{array}{r}6\\+9\\\hline\end{array}$ |

| $\begin{array}{r}9\\+8\\\hline\end{array}$ | $\begin{array}{r}8\\+8\\\hline\end{array}$ | $\begin{array}{r}9\\+7\\\hline\end{array}$ | $\begin{array}{r}8\\+7\\\hline\end{array}$ | $\begin{array}{r}9\\+5\\\hline\end{array}$ | $\begin{array}{r}7\\+7\\\hline\end{array}$ |

| $\begin{array}{r}9\\+3\\\hline\end{array}$ | $\begin{array}{r}8\\+5\\\hline\end{array}$ | $\begin{array}{r}7\\+6\\\hline\end{array}$ | $\begin{array}{r}8\\+6\\\hline\end{array}$ | $\begin{array}{r}9\\+4\\\hline\end{array}$ | $\begin{array}{r}7\\+5\\\hline\end{array}$ |

Problem Solving

Solve each problem.

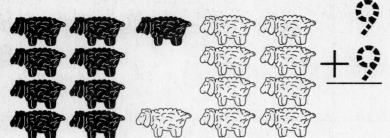 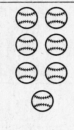

_____ black sheep

_____ white sheep

_____ sheep in all

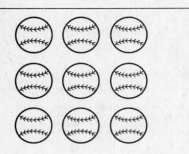

_____ softballs

_____ baseballs

_____ balls in all

_____ glasses of milk

_____ empty glasses

_____ glasses in all

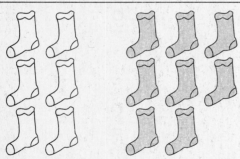

_____ white socks

_____ gray socks

_____ socks in all

_____ bow ties

_____ regular ties

_____ ties in all

Lesson 6 Subtraction Facts Through 18

Subtract.

$$\begin{array}{r} 1\ 5 \\ -\ 7 \\ \hline 8 \end{array}$$

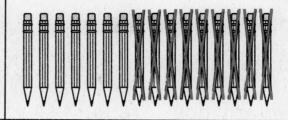

$$\begin{array}{r} 1\ 6 \\ -\ 9 \\ \hline \end{array}$$

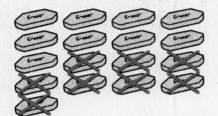

$$\begin{array}{r} 1\ 7 \\ -\ 8 \\ \hline \end{array}$$

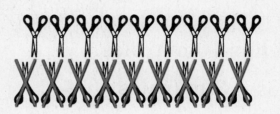

$$\begin{array}{r} 1\ 8 \\ -\ 9 \\ \hline \end{array}$$

Subtract.

$$\begin{array}{r} 1\ 8 \\ -\ 9 \\ \hline 9 \end{array}$$
$$\begin{array}{r} 1\ 3 \\ -\ 5 \\ \hline \end{array}$$
$$\begin{array}{r} 1\ 6 \\ -\ 8 \\ \hline \end{array}$$
$$\begin{array}{r} 1\ 7 \\ -\ 9 \\ \hline \end{array}$$
$$\begin{array}{r} 1\ 4 \\ -\ 6 \\ \hline \end{array}$$
$$\begin{array}{r} 1\ 3 \\ -\ 9 \\ \hline \end{array}$$

$$\begin{array}{r} 1\ 7 \\ -\ 8 \\ \hline \end{array}$$
$$\begin{array}{r} 1\ 5 \\ -\ 9 \\ \hline \end{array}$$
$$\begin{array}{r} 1\ 4 \\ -\ 5 \\ \hline \end{array}$$
$$\begin{array}{r} 1\ 3 \\ -\ 6 \\ \hline \end{array}$$
$$\begin{array}{r} 1\ 6 \\ -\ 7 \\ \hline \end{array}$$
$$\begin{array}{r} 1\ 2 \\ -\ 4 \\ \hline \end{array}$$

$$\begin{array}{r} 1\ 4 \\ -\ 7 \\ \hline \end{array}$$
$$\begin{array}{r} 1\ 5 \\ -\ 8 \\ \hline \end{array}$$
$$\begin{array}{r} 1\ 6 \\ -\ 9 \\ \hline \end{array}$$
$$\begin{array}{r} 1\ 2 \\ -\ 7 \\ \hline \end{array}$$
$$\begin{array}{r} 1\ 5 \\ -\ 7 \\ \hline \end{array}$$
$$\begin{array}{r} 1\ 3 \\ -\ 4 \\ \hline \end{array}$$

$$\begin{array}{r} 1\ 5 \\ -\ 6 \\ \hline \end{array}$$
$$\begin{array}{r} 1\ 4 \\ -\ 8 \\ \hline \end{array}$$
$$\begin{array}{r} 1\ 2 \\ -\ 3 \\ \hline \end{array}$$
$$\begin{array}{r} 1\ 3 \\ -\ 9 \\ \hline \end{array}$$
$$\begin{array}{r} 1\ 4 \\ -\ 9 \\ \hline \end{array}$$
$$\begin{array}{r} 1\ 1 \\ -\ 3 \\ \hline \end{array}$$

Solve each problem.

There are 12 dogs.

3 run away.

How many dogs are left?

$$\begin{array}{r} 12 \\ -\ 3 \\ \hline 9 \end{array}$$

Josh has 10 marbles.

He loses 3 marbles.

How many marbles are left?

Lauren has 16 black shoes.

Mike has 8 black shoes.

How many more shoes does Lauren have than Mike?

There are 14 cows in the field.

9 cows come to the barn.

How many cows are left in the field?

There are 18 horses running.

There are 9 horses standing.

How many more horses are running than standing?

Lesson 7   Mixed Practice Facts Through 18

Add.

9	5	7	4	9	7
+7	+9	+8	+9	+9	+7
16					

6	8	9	7	8	7
+9	+6	+5	+9	+9	+6

8	6	9	8	9	8
+8	+8	+6	+5	+8	+7

Subtract.

16	10	16	12	14	16
− 9	− 8	− 8	− 6	− 8	− 7
7					

11	14	15	12	17	10
− 7	− 9	− 9	− 8	− 8	− 5

14	17	13	15	18	13
− 7	− 9	− 7	− 8	− 9	− 8

Solve each problem.

Michelle has 18 tickets.

She uses 9 of them.

How many tickets are left?

Jeff buys 14 nails.

He uses 6 of them.

How many are left?

There are 10 people on the train.

7 more get on.

How many people are on the train?

Tony has 13 pencils in his desk.

He takes 4 pencils out of his desk.

How many pencils are left in his desk?

Emily's house has 7 windows in it.

Jamie's house has 9 windows in it.

How many windows do Emily's and Jamie's houses have in all?

Lesson 8 Addition and Subtraction

Add or subtract.

If you get 9, color the part red.
If you get 14, color the part brown.

$$\begin{array}{r} 9 \\ -7 \\ \hline \end{array}$$

$$\begin{array}{r} 3 \\ +4 \\ \hline \end{array}$$

$$\begin{array}{r} 1\ 2 \\ -\ 8 \\ \hline \end{array}$$

$5 + 5 =$ _____

$11 - 7 =$ _____

$$\begin{array}{r} 1\ 5 \\ -\ 8 \\ \hline \end{array}$$

$$\begin{array}{r} 7 \\ +5 \\ \hline \end{array}$$

$$\begin{array}{r} 1\ 4 \\ -\ 9 \\ \hline \end{array}$$

$14 - 5 =$ _____

$7 - 6 =$ _____

$$\begin{array}{r} 8 \\ +6 \\ \hline \end{array}$$

$$\begin{array}{r} 6 \\ -5 \\ \hline \end{array}$$

$$\begin{array}{r} 1\ 8 \\ -\ 9 \\ \hline \end{array}$$

$$\begin{array}{r} 1\ 1 \\ -\ 3 \\ \hline \end{array}$$

$$\begin{array}{r} 6 \\ +3 \\ \hline \end{array}$$

$4 + 8 =$ _____

$$\begin{array}{r} 1\ 3 \\ -4 \\ \hline \end{array}$$

$$\begin{array}{r} 2 \\ +7 \\ \hline \end{array}$$

$$\begin{array}{r} 1\ 7 \\ -\ 8 \\ \hline \end{array}$$

$$\begin{array}{r} 4 \\ +5 \\ \hline \end{array}$$

$$\begin{array}{r} 1\ 6 \\ -\ 7 \\ \hline \end{array}$$

$$\begin{array}{r} 1\ 2 \\ -\ 3 \\ \hline \end{array}$$

$$\begin{array}{r} 1\ 5 \\ -\ 6 \\ \hline \end{array}$$

$$\begin{array}{r} 1\ 3 \\ -\ 8 \\ \hline \end{array}$$

$$\begin{array}{r} 5 \\ +9 \\ \hline \end{array}$$

$$\begin{array}{r} 6 \\ +8 \\ \hline \end{array}$$

$$\begin{array}{r} 5 \\ +6 \\ \hline \end{array}$$

$$\begin{array}{r} 1\ 0 \\ -\ 7 \\ \hline \end{array}$$

$$\begin{array}{r} 6 \\ +6 \\ \hline \end{array}$$

$$\begin{array}{r} 7 \\ +7 \\ \hline \end{array}$$

$$\begin{array}{r} 8 \\ +9 \\ \hline \end{array}$$

$$\begin{array}{r} 1\ 1 \\ -\ 5 \\ \hline \end{array}$$

$$\begin{array}{r} 9 \\ +5 \\ \hline \end{array}$$

$$\begin{array}{r} 9 \\ +7 \\ \hline \end{array}$$

$$\begin{array}{r} 8 \\ +8 \\ \hline \end{array}$$

SPECTRUM MATHEMATICS,
Brown Book

Solve each problem.

Mallory needed 17 balloons for a party.

Mallory had 8 balloons at home.

How many more balloons did she need?

Alex had 9 white cowboy hats.

He also had 7 black cowboy hats.

How many cowboy hats did Alex have?

The office helper had 18 letters to write.

She wrote 9.

How many more letters did she have to write?

Dave read 8 books at school.

Kellie read 7 books at school.

How many books did Dave and Kellie read in all?

Craig had 16 bolts.

He used 8 of the bolts.

How many bolts did Craig have left?

CHAPTER 3 CHECKUP

Add.

5	6	9	8	5	7
+8	+7	+5	+9	+6	+7

7	9	6	9	8	7
+6	+9	+9	+7	+8	+8

Subtract.

1 2	1 6	1 1	1 3	1 5	1 4
− 7	− 8	− 8	− 9	− 7	− 9

1 8	1 3	1 7	1 4	1 2	1 3
− 9	− 4	− 9	− 5	− 9	− 6

Solve each problem.

_____ tomatoes on vine

_____ tomatoes on ground

_____ tomatoes in all

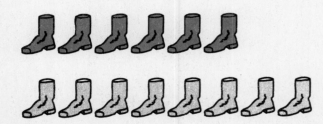

_____ boots in all

_____ gray boots

_____ blue boots

PRE-TEST

Ring the fraction that tells how much is blue.

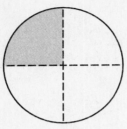
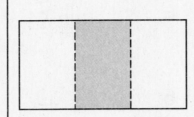
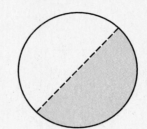

$\frac{1}{3}$ $\frac{1}{2}$ $\frac{1}{4}$ $\frac{1}{2}$ $\frac{1}{3}$ $\frac{1}{4}$ $\frac{1}{4}$ $\frac{1}{3}$ $\frac{1}{2}$

Write the time for each clock.

_____ o'clock   half past _____   _____ o'clock

Use a centimeter ruler.
How long is each object?

____ centimeters

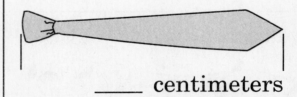

____ centimeters

Use an inch ruler.
How long is each object?

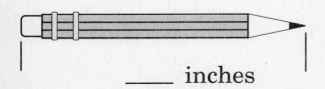

____ inches

____ inches

SPECTRUM MATHEMATICS,
Brown Book

4

Lesson 1 One-Half

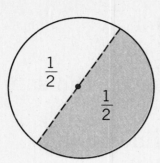

$\frac{1}{2}$ $\frac{1}{2}$

 part is blue.

The 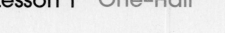 parts are the same size.

 of the inside is blue.

Complete.

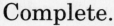

 part is blue.

 parts are the same size.

 of the inside is blue.

___ part is blue.

___ parts are the same size.

___ of the inside is blue.

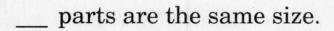

___ part is blue.

___ parts are the same size.

___ of the inside is blue.

___ part is blue.

___ parts are the same size.

___ of the inside is blue.

___ of the inside is blue.

___ of the inside is blue.

Lesson 2 One-Third

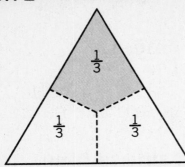

 part is blue.

The parts are the same size.

 of the inside is blue.

Complete.

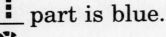

 part is blue.

parts are the same size.

of the inside is blue.

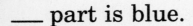

___ part is blue.

___ parts are the same size.

___ of the inside is blue.

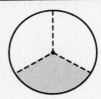

___ part is blue.

___ parts are the same size.

___ of the inside is blue.

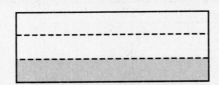

___ part is blue.

___ parts are the same size.

___ of the inside is blue.

___ of the inside is blue.

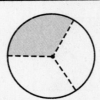

___ of the inside is blue.

Lesson 3 One-Fourth

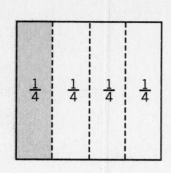

$\frac{1}{4}$ $\frac{1}{4}$ $\frac{1}{4}$ $\frac{1}{4}$

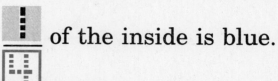 part is blue.

The 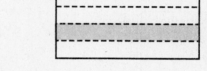 parts are the same size.

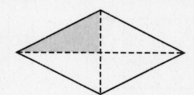 of the inside is blue.

Complete.

 part is blue.

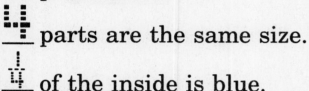 parts are the same size.

___ of the inside is blue.

___ part is blue.

___ parts are the same size.

___ of the inside is blue.

___ part is blue.

___ parts are the same size.

___ of the inside is blue.

___ part is blue.

___ parts are the same size.

___ of the inside is blue.

---

 of the inside is blue.

 of the inside is blue.

Fractions

Ring the fraction that tells how much is blue.

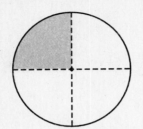

$\frac{1}{2}$ $\frac{1}{3}$ $\boxed{\frac{1}{4}}$

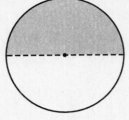

$\frac{1}{2}$ $\frac{1}{3}$ $\frac{1}{4}$

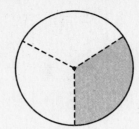

$\frac{1}{2}$ $\frac{1}{3}$ $\frac{1}{4}$

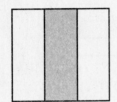

$\frac{1}{2}$ $\frac{1}{3}$ $\frac{1}{4}$

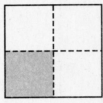

$\frac{1}{2}$ $\frac{1}{3}$ $\frac{1}{4}$

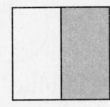

$\frac{1}{2}$ $\frac{1}{3}$ $\frac{1}{4}$

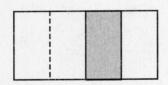

$\frac{1}{2}$ $\frac{1}{3}$ $\frac{1}{4}$

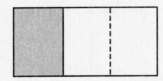

$\frac{1}{2}$ $\frac{1}{3}$ $\frac{1}{4}$

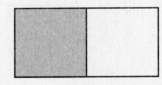

$\frac{1}{2}$ $\frac{1}{3}$ $\frac{1}{4}$

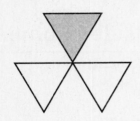

$\frac{1}{2}$ $\frac{1}{3}$ $\frac{1}{4}$

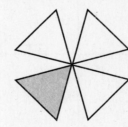

$\frac{1}{2}$ $\frac{1}{3}$ $\frac{1}{4}$

$\frac{1}{2}$ $\frac{1}{3}$ $\frac{1}{4}$

SPECTRUM MATHEMATICS,
Brown Book

Lesson 4 Time—Hour

 8 o'clock

8:00

Both clocks show the same time.

Write the time for each clock.

___4___ o'clock

__4__ : **:00**

_____ o'clock

____ : **:00**

_____ o'clock

____ : **:00**

 9:00

_____ o'clock

____ : ____

3:00

_____ o'clock

____ : ____

11:00

_____ o'clock

____ : ____

_____ o'clock

____ : ____

_____ o'clock

____ : ____

_____ o'clock

____ : ____

Lesson 5 Time—Half Hour

2 o'clock
2:00

half past 2
2:30

3 o'clock
3:00

Write the time for each clock.

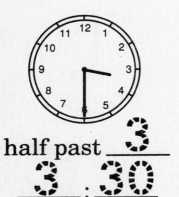

half past __3__

__3__ : __30__

half past _____

_____ : __30__

half past _____

_____ : __30__

10:30

half past _____

_____ : _____

4:30

half past _____

_____ : _____

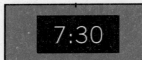

7:30

half past _____

_____ : _____

half past _____

_____ : _____

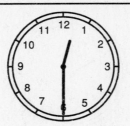

half past _____

_____ : _____

half past _____

_____ : _____

Lesson 6 Time

Show this time on this clock. Show this time on this clock.

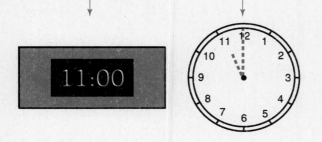

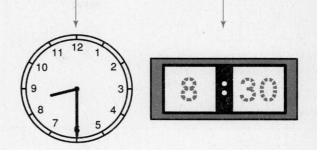

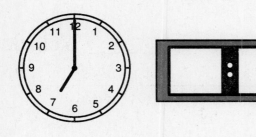

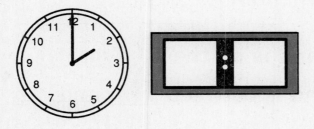

Solve each problem.

 The short hand is on the

The long hand is on the

The time is _____ o'clock.

 The short hand is on the

The long hand is on the

The time is _____ o'clock.

 The long hand is on the

The short hand is on the

The time is _____ o'clock.

 The short hand is on the

The long hand is on the

The time is _____ o'clock.

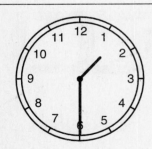 The long hand is on the

The short hand is between _____ and _____.

The time is _____:_____.

Lesson 7 Calendar

	OCTOBER					
S	**M**	**T**	**W**	**T**	**F**	**S**
1	2	3	4	5	6	7
8	9	10	11	12	13	14
15	16	17	18	19	20	21
22	23	24	25	26	27	28
29	30	31				

Complete.

How many days are in October? _____

How many Saturdays are in October? _____

How many days are in 1 week? _____

How many days are in 2 weeks? _____

How many Tuesdays are in October? _____

What day of the week is the 26th? _____

JANUARY						
S	M	T	W	T	F	S
1	2	3	4	5	6	7
8	9	10	11	12	13	14
15	16	17	18	19	20	21
22	23	24	25	26	27	28
29	30	31				

FEBRUARY						
S	M	T	W	T	F	S
			1	2	3	4
5	6	7	8	9	10	11
12	13	14	15	16	17	18
19	20	21	22	23	24	25
26	27	28				

MARCH						
S	M	T	W	T	F	S
			1	2	3	4
5	6	7	8	9	10	11
12	13	14	15	16	17	18
19	20	21	22	23	24	25
26	27	28	29	30	31	

APRIL						
S	M	T	W	T	F	S
						1
2	3	4	5	6	7	8
9	10	11	12	13	14	15
16	17	18	19	20	21	22
23/30	24	25	26	27	28	29

MAY						
S	M	T	W	T	F	S
	1	2	3	4	5	6
7	8	9	10	11	12	13
14	15	16	17	18	19	20
21	22	23	24	25	26	27
28	29	30	31			

JUNE						
S	M	T	W	T	F	S
				1	2	3
4	5	6	7	8	9	10
11	12	13	14	15	16	17
18	19	20	21	22	23	24
25	26	27	28	29	30	

JULY						
S	M	T	W	T	F	S
						1
2	3	4	5	6	7	8
9	10	11	12	13	14	15
16	17	18	19	20	21	22
23/30	24/31	25	26	27	28	29

AUGUST						
S	M	T	W	T	F	S
		1	2	3	4	5
6	7	8	9	10	11	12
13	14	15	16	17	18	19
20	21	22	23	24	25	26
27	28	29	30	31		

SEPTEMBER						
S	M	T	W	T	F	S
					1	2
3	4	5	6	7	8	9
10	11	12	13	14	15	16
17	18	19	20	21	22	23
24	25	26	27	28	29	30

OCTOBER						
S	M	T	W	T	F	S
1	2	3	4	5	6	7
8	9	10	11	12	13	14
15	16	17	18	19	20	21
22	23	24	25	26	27	28
29	30	31				

NOVEMBER						
S	M	T	W	T	F	S
			1	2	3	4
5	6	7	8	9	10	11
12	13	14	15	16	17	18
19	20	21	22	23	24	25
26	27	28	29	30		

DECEMBER						
S	M	T	W	T	F	S
					1	2
3	4	5	6	7	8	9
10	11	12	13	14	15	16
17	18	19	20	21	22	23
24/31	25	26	27	28	29	30

Complete.

How many months are in 1 year? _____

How many months have exactly 30 days? _____

How many months have 31 days? _____

Which month has only 28 days? _____

How many months begin with the letter J? _____

How many months have 5 Saturdays? _____

Lesson 8   Centimeter

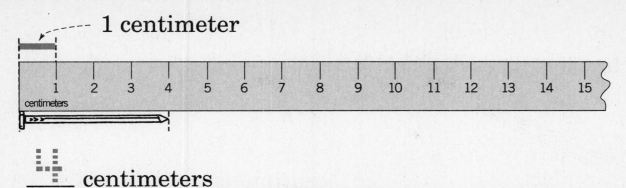

1 centimeter

4 centimeters

How long is each object?

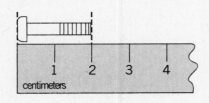

_____ centimeters

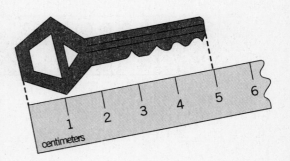

_____ centimeters

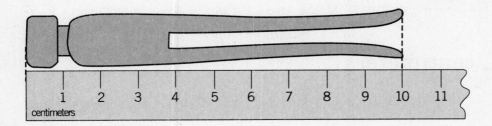

_____ centimeters

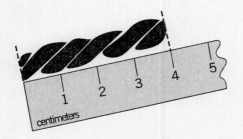

_____ centimeters

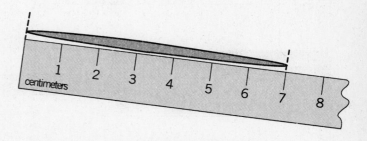

_____ centimeters

← Cut off this ruler.
How long is each object?

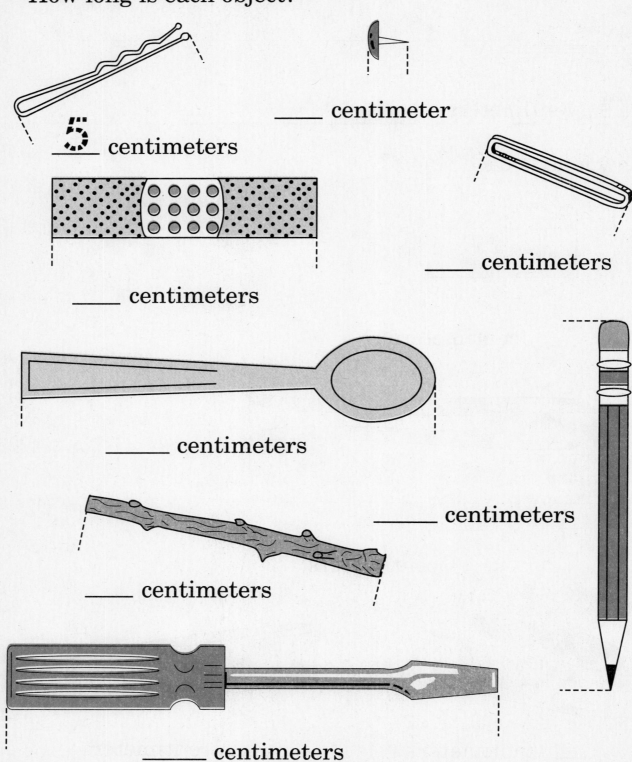

_____ centimeter

_5_ centimeters

_____ centimeters

_____ centimeters

_____ centimeters

_____ centimeters

_____ centimeters

_____ centimeters

SPECTRUM MATHEMATICS,
Brown Book

Lesson 9   Inch

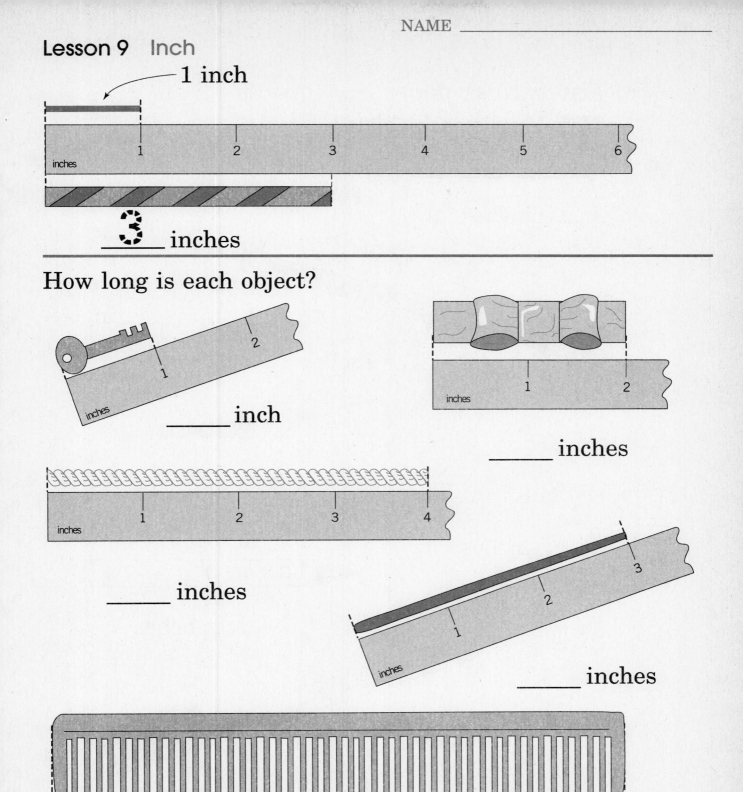

1 inch

_____ inches

How long is each object?

_____ inch

_____ inches

_____ inches

_____ inches

_____ inches

Inch

← Cut off this ruler.
How long is each object?

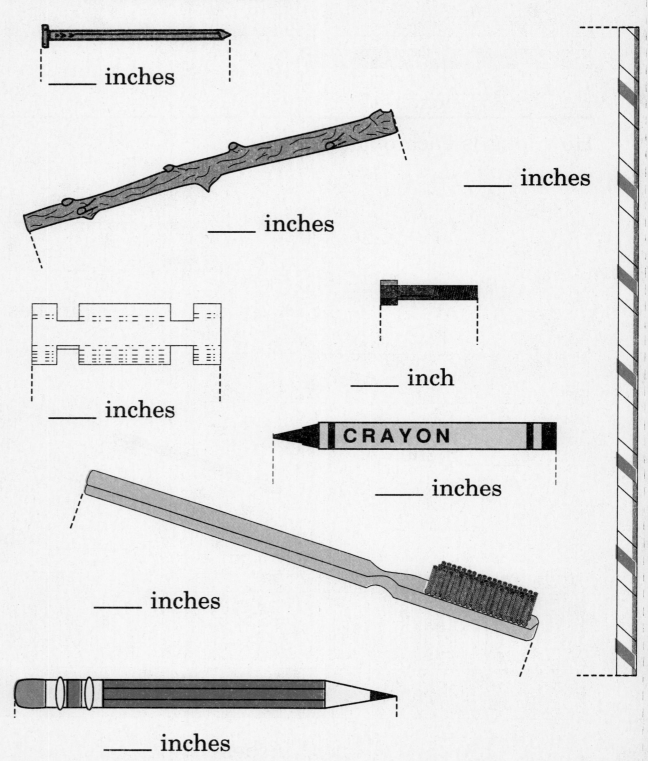

_____ inches

_____ inches

_____ inches

_____ inches

_____ inch

_____ inches

CRAYON

_____ inches

_____ inches

_____ inches

CHAPTER 4   CHECKUP

Use a centimeter ruler.

How long is each object?

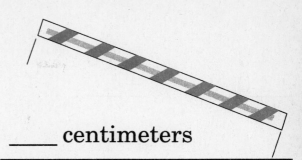

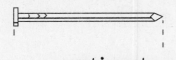

_____ centimeters

_____ centimeters

Ring the fraction that tells how much is blue.

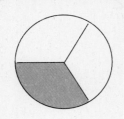

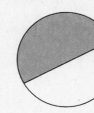

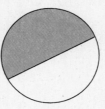

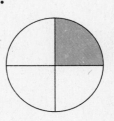

$\frac{1}{2}$ $\frac{1}{3}$ $\frac{1}{4}$ $\frac{1}{2}$ $\frac{1}{3}$ $\frac{1}{4}$ $\frac{1}{2}$ $\frac{1}{3}$ $\frac{1}{4}$

Use an inch ruler.

How long is each object?

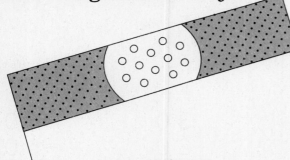

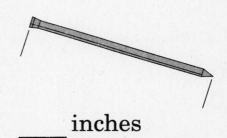

_____ inches

_____ inches

Write the time for each clock.

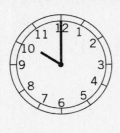

____ : ____

____ : ____

____ : ____

PRE-TEST

Add.

20	30	60	70	40
+30	+40	+30	+10	+10

55	60	70	82	93
+23	+15	+12	+15	+ 3

4	2	20	40	30
2	2	10	20	40
+1	+2	+30	+10	+20

Subtract.

40	60	70	30	80
−10	−20	−40	−20	−50

85	76	99	65	53
−24	−23	−33	−14	−20

SPECTRUM MATHEMATICS,
Brown Book

Lesson 1   Addition and Subtraction Review

Add.

9 +8	6 +6	7 +9	5 +7	9 +9	4 +8
7 +6	6 +9	8 +6	7 +7	5 +8	8 +2
9 +4	7 +8	5 +5	9 +1	3 +9	5 +6

Subtract.

1 8 − 9	1 1 − 9	1 0 − 5	1 2 − 4	1 3 − 7	1 4 − 9
1 0 − 6	1 2 − 7	1 3 − 5	1 1 − 3	1 5 − 8	1 0 − 9
1 4 − 7	1 1 − 6	1 5 − 7	1 7 − 9	1 2 − 8	1 3 − 4

Addition and Subtraction Review

Ring each name for the number in the ◯.

◯11

$4 + 8$

(5 + 6)

(9 + 2)

(4 + 7)

(8 + 3) $6 + 6$

◯16

$5 + 7$

$8 + 7$ $6 + 9$

$7 + 9$ $9 + 7$

$8 + 8$

◯15

$7 + 8$

$7 + 7$

$8 + 7$ $6 + 9$

$5 + 9$

$9 + 6$

◯13

$8 + 5$

$6 + 8$ $7 + 6$

$9 + 4$ $9 + 5$

$6 + 7$ $4 + 8$

◯7

$13 - 6$

$17 - 8$

$15 - 8$ $16 - 9$

$14 - 7$ $14 - 6$

◯8

$17 - 9$ $15 - 7$ $10 - 6$

$12 - 4$ $13 - 5$ $11 - 7$

$11 - 3$

◯6

$13 - 7$

$15 - 6$ $14 - 8$

$16 - 7$

$12 - 6$ $12 - 8$

◯9

$17 - 9$

$13 - 4$

$16 - 7$ $11 - 5$

$15 - 7$ $12 - 8$ $18 - 9$

SPECTRUM MATHEMATICS,
Brown Book

Lesson 2   Adding Tens

3 tens	3 0		6 tens	6 0
+4 tens	+4 0		+2 tens	+2 0
7 tens	7 0		8 tens	80

Add.

2 tens	2 0		5 tens	5 0
+4 tens	+4 0		+3 tens	+3 0
tens			tens	

2 0	1 0	4 0	3 0	5 0
+2 0	+5 0	+2 0	+4 0	+3 0

3 0	6 0	2 0	7 0	1 0
+2 0	+1 0	+5 0	+1 0	+1 0

1 0	4 0	8 0	6 0	2 0
+2 0	+4 0	+1 0	+3 0	+6 0

7 0	4 0	3 0	5 0	3 0
+2 0	+1 0	+1 0	+4 0	+3 0

Solve each problem.

There are 20 men in the plane.

30 women get in the plane.

How many men and women are in the plane?

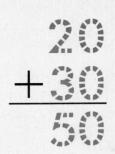

$$\begin{array}{r} 20 \\ + 30 \\ \hline 50 \end{array}$$

Jill buys 10 apples.

Kara buys 20 apples.

How many apples in all?

There are 30 ears of corn in one pile.

There are 50 ears of corn in another pile.

How many ears of corn in all?

Jeremy cut 40 pieces of wood.

Caleb cut 20 pieces of wood.

How many pieces of wood were cut?

Adolpho had 60 baseball cards.

Maria had 30 baseball cards.

How many baseball cards in all?

Lesson 3   Addition

Join the pennies.
Add the ones.

$$\begin{array}{r} 34 \\ +23 \\ \hline 7 \end{array}$$

Join the dimes.
Add the tens.

$$\begin{array}{r} 34 \\ +23 \\ \hline 57 \end{array}$$

Add.

$$\begin{array}{r} 2\,3 \\ +1\,4 \\ \hline 3\,7 \end{array} \qquad \begin{array}{r} 5\,5 \\ +\ 2 \\ \hline \end{array} \qquad \begin{array}{r} 7\,0 \\ +2\,3 \\ \hline \end{array} \qquad \begin{array}{r} 6\,0 \\ +1\,3 \\ \hline \end{array}$$

↑ ↑ Add the ones.
└─ Add the tens.

$$\begin{array}{r} 4\,3 \\ +5\,2 \\ \hline \end{array} \qquad \begin{array}{r} 3\,6 \\ +2\,1 \\ \hline \end{array} \qquad \begin{array}{r} 4\,5 \\ +1\,3 \\ \hline \end{array} \qquad \begin{array}{r} 8\,3 \\ +1\,2 \\ \hline \end{array} \qquad \begin{array}{r} 2\,6 \\ +4\,3 \\ \hline \end{array}$$

$$\begin{array}{r} 5\,3 \\ +4\,2 \\ \hline \end{array} \qquad \begin{array}{r} 3\,8 \\ +3\,1 \\ \hline \end{array} \qquad \begin{array}{r} 8\,1 \\ +\ 3 \\ \hline \end{array} \qquad \begin{array}{r} 3\,3 \\ +5\,3 \\ \hline \end{array} \qquad \begin{array}{r} 7\,5 \\ +2\,2 \\ \hline \end{array}$$

$$\begin{array}{r} 7\,1 \\ +2\,7 \\ \hline \end{array} \qquad \begin{array}{r} 6\,2 \\ +1\,4 \\ \hline \end{array} \qquad \begin{array}{r} 6\,7 \\ +2\,2 \\ \hline \end{array} \qquad \begin{array}{r} 4\,3 \\ +4\,6 \\ \hline \end{array} \qquad \begin{array}{r} 3\,4 \\ +3\,0 \\ \hline \end{array}$$

$$\begin{array}{r} 3\,1 \\ +5\,0 \\ \hline \end{array} \qquad \begin{array}{r} 6\,0 \\ +3\,2 \\ \hline \end{array} \qquad \begin{array}{r} 5\,4 \\ +2\,0 \\ \hline \end{array} \qquad \begin{array}{r} 4\,7 \\ +3\,0 \\ \hline \end{array} \qquad \begin{array}{r} 4\,0 \\ +4\,0 \\ \hline \end{array}$$

Solve each problem.

Pablo sees 25 🐦.

Scott sees 34 🐦.

How many 🐦 in all?

$$25 \\ +34$$

Lindsay bought 14 📓.

Paul bought 12 📓.

How many 📓 in all?

Paco drinks 21 🥛 a week.

Lee drinks 28 🥛 a week.

How many 🥛 do they drink in 1 week?

June has 31 ✏.

Melody has 24 ✏.

How many ✏ in all?

Brittany peeled 41 🥔.

Jason peeled 37 🥔.

How many 🥔 did they peel?

Lesson 4   Addition (2-digit)

Add.

$$\begin{array}{r} 4\ 5 \\ +3\ 2 \\ \hline 77 \end{array}\qquad \begin{array}{r} 5\ 2 \\ +2\ 4 \\ \hline 76 \end{array}\qquad \begin{array}{r} 4\ 0 \\ +1\ 0 \\ \hline \end{array}\qquad \begin{array}{r} 2\ 2 \\ +2\ 2 \\ \hline \end{array}\qquad \begin{array}{r} 6\ 5 \\ +1\ 3 \\ \hline \end{array}$$

$$\begin{array}{r} 1\ 4 \\ +5\ 1 \\ \hline \end{array}\qquad \begin{array}{r} 1\ 8 \\ +4\ 1 \\ \hline \end{array}\qquad \begin{array}{r} 6\ 3 \\ +3\ 1 \\ \hline \end{array}\qquad \begin{array}{r} 3\ 4 \\ +5\ 1 \\ \hline \end{array}\qquad \begin{array}{r} 4\ 6 \\ +3\ 2 \\ \hline \end{array}$$

$$\begin{array}{r} 2\ 3 \\ +5\ 4 \\ \hline \end{array}\qquad \begin{array}{r} 4\ 4 \\ +4\ 2 \\ \hline \end{array}\qquad \begin{array}{r} 6\ 2 \\ +3\ 5 \\ \hline \end{array}\qquad \begin{array}{r} 7\ 3 \\ +2\ 5 \\ \hline \end{array}\qquad \begin{array}{r} 8\ 0 \\ +1\ 5 \\ \hline \end{array}$$

$$\begin{array}{r} 6\ 4 \\ +1\ 5 \\ \hline \end{array}\qquad \begin{array}{r} 1\ 5 \\ +2\ 2 \\ \hline \end{array}\qquad \begin{array}{r} 3\ 3 \\ +3\ 3 \\ \hline \end{array}\qquad \begin{array}{r} 8\ 2 \\ +1\ 7 \\ \hline \end{array}\qquad \begin{array}{r} 7\ 1 \\ +2\ 5 \\ \hline \end{array}$$

$$\begin{array}{r} 2\ 6 \\ +3\ 3 \\ \hline \end{array}\qquad \begin{array}{r} 1\ 8 \\ +3\ 1 \\ \hline \end{array}\qquad \begin{array}{r} 4\ 3 \\ +1\ 2 \\ \hline \end{array}\qquad \begin{array}{r} 2\ 4 \\ +2\ 4 \\ \hline \end{array}\qquad \begin{array}{r} 5\ 5 \\ +2\ 3 \\ \hline \end{array}$$

$$\begin{array}{r} 7\ 2 \\ +2\ 4 \\ \hline \end{array}\qquad \begin{array}{r} 6\ 6 \\ +3\ 2 \\ \hline \end{array}\qquad \begin{array}{r} 5\ 4 \\ +1\ 1 \\ \hline \end{array}\qquad \begin{array}{r} 1\ 1 \\ +1\ 1 \\ \hline \end{array}\qquad \begin{array}{r} 2\ 5 \\ +2\ 4 \\ \hline \end{array}$$

Ken has	Jill has	Pam has	Rod has
25¢	26¢	20¢	32¢

Complete.

Who has the most money? _____

Who has the least money? _____

Solve each problem.

Ken has	**25**¢	Pam has	**20**¢
Pam has	**+20**¢	Rod has	**+32**¢
Ken and Pam have	**45**¢	Pam and Rod have	¢

Jill has	¢	Rod has	¢
Pam has	+___¢	Jill has	+___¢
Jill and Pam have	¢	Rod and Jill have	¢

Ken has	¢	Pam has	¢
Rod has	+___¢	Ken has	+___¢
Ken and Rod have	¢	Pam and Ken have	¢

Lesson 5   Subtracting Tens

6 tens	6 0		8 tens	8 0
−3 tens	−3 0		−2 tens	−2 0
3 tens	3 0		6 tens	60

Subtract.

7 tens	7 0		4 tens	4 0
−5 tens	−5 0		−2 tens	−2 0
___ tens			___ tens	

5 0	6 0	2 0	8 0	4 0
−3 0	−2 0	−1 0	−4 0	−4 0

9 0	8 0	7 0	3 0	5 0
−5 0	−2 0	−3 0	−2 0	−4 0

6 0	4 0	8 0	9 0	7 0
−3 0	−1 0	−3 0	−2 0	−5 0

8 0	9 0	7 0	6 0	5 0
−7 0	−8 0	−4 0	−4 0	−2 0

Solve each problem.

Mr. Cobb counts 70 .

He sells 30 .

How many are left?

Keith has 20 .

Leon has 10 .

How many more does Keith have?

Tina planted 60 .

Melody planted 30 .

How many more   did Tina plant?

Link has 80 .

Jessica has 50 .

How many more does Link have?

Maranda hits 40 .

Harold hits 30 .

How many more does Maranda hit?

Lesson 6 Subtraction (2-digit)

Take away 1 penny.
Subtract the ones.

$$\begin{array}{r} 53 \\ -21 \\ \hline 2 \end{array}$$

Take away 2 dimes.
Subtract the tens.

$$\begin{array}{r} 53 \\ -21 \\ \hline 32 \end{array}$$

Subtract.

$$\begin{array}{r} 79 \\ -6 \\ \hline 73 \end{array}$$

$$\begin{array}{r} 82 \\ -52 \\ \hline 30 \end{array}$$

$$\begin{array}{r} 65 \\ -24 \\ \hline \end{array}$$

$$\begin{array}{r} 56 \\ -26 \\ \hline \end{array}$$

— Subtract the ones.
— Subtract the tens.

$$\begin{array}{r} 87 \\ -23 \\ \hline \end{array}$$

$$\begin{array}{r} 36 \\ -20 \\ \hline \end{array}$$

$$\begin{array}{r} 94 \\ -1 \\ \hline \end{array}$$

$$\begin{array}{r} 58 \\ -17 \\ \hline \end{array}$$

$$\begin{array}{r} 65 \\ -51 \\ \hline \end{array}$$

$$\begin{array}{r} 57 \\ -10 \\ \hline \end{array}$$

$$\begin{array}{r} 89 \\ -64 \\ \hline \end{array}$$

$$\begin{array}{r} 46 \\ -3 \\ \hline \end{array}$$

$$\begin{array}{r} 75 \\ -15 \\ \hline \end{array}$$

$$\begin{array}{r} 37 \\ -24 \\ \hline \end{array}$$

$$\begin{array}{r} 46 \\ -34 \\ \hline \end{array}$$

$$\begin{array}{r} 78 \\ -68 \\ \hline \end{array}$$

$$\begin{array}{r} 29 \\ -2 \\ \hline \end{array}$$

$$\begin{array}{r} 85 \\ -43 \\ \hline \end{array}$$

$$\begin{array}{r} 78 \\ -21 \\ \hline \end{array}$$

$$\begin{array}{r} 79 \\ -61 \\ \hline \end{array}$$

$$\begin{array}{r} 97 \\ -65 \\ \hline \end{array}$$

$$\begin{array}{r} 84 \\ -2 \\ \hline \end{array}$$

$$\begin{array}{r} 65 \\ -22 \\ \hline \end{array}$$

$$\begin{array}{r} 99 \\ -37 \\ \hline \end{array}$$

Maria has	Pedro has	Anna has	Leroy has
45¢	42¢	65¢	32¢

Solve each problem.

Anna has	65¢	Maria has	¢
Pedro has	− 42¢	Pedro has	− ¢
Anna has this much more.	23¢	Maria has this much more.	¢

Pedro has	¢	Anna has	¢
Leroy has	− ¢	Leroy has	− ¢
Pedro has this much more.	¢	Anna has this much more.	¢

Anna has	¢	Maria has	¢
Maria has	− ¢	Leroy has	− ¢
Anna has this much more.	¢	Maria has this much more.	¢

Lesson 7 Adding Three Numbers

Add the ones.

$$
\begin{array}{r}
12 \\
53 \\
+24 \\
\hline
9
\end{array}
\qquad
\begin{array}{r}
5 \\
+4 \\
\hline
\end{array}
$$

Add the tens.

$$
\begin{array}{r}
60 \\
+20 \\
\hline
\end{array}
\qquad
\begin{array}{r}
12 \\
53 \\
+24 \\
\hline
89
\end{array}
$$

Add.

1	2	3	4	2	3
6	4	5	1	2	3
+1	+2	+0	+4	+5	+3
8					

30	20	20	30	40
10	30	20	20	30
+10	+10	+20	+0	+10
50				

31	14	66	15	41
16	10	20	51	14
+11	+11	+13	+1	+12
58				

33	31	54	71	32
21	12	12	17	21
+23	+51	+21	+1	+32

Why did the bird fly south?

A	F	I	K	L	O	R	S	T	W
7	9	35	39	47	58	59	68	86	88

Add. Write the letter for each answer.

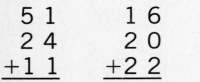

```
  1 2     4 3              3 0       3       2 5
  1 2     2 2              2 4       2       3 1
+ 1 1   + 2 1           + 3 4     + 2     + 1 2
```
35

  ☐ ☐ ☐ ☐

```
  5 1     1 6     3 1       3       1       1 3
  2 4     2 0     1 6       3       2       2 4
+ 1 1   + 2 2   + 1 1     + 3     + 4     + 2 2
```

☐ ☐ ☐ ☐ ☐ ☐

```
  6 3     3 0            5 1       3       1 4       1 3
  1 0     1 7            2 6       3       2 3       1 1
+ 1 3   + 1 1          + 1 1     + 1     + 1 0     + 1 5
```

☐ ☐

SPECTRUM MATHEMATICS,
Brown Book

Lesson 8   Money
half-dollar

50¢

50¢

50¢

Tell how many cents there are.

$$\begin{array}{r} 50\,¢ \\ +\ 25\,¢ \\ \hline 75\,¢ \end{array}$$

$$\begin{array}{r} 50\,¢ \\ +\ 30\,¢ \\ \hline \,¢ \end{array}$$

$$\begin{array}{r} \,¢ \\ +\ \,¢ \\ \hline \,¢ \end{array}$$

$$\begin{array}{r} \,¢ \\ +\ \,¢ \\ \hline \,¢ \end{array}$$

$$\begin{array}{r} 50\,¢ \\ 25\,¢ \\ +\ 10\,¢ \\ \hline \,¢ \end{array}$$

$$\begin{array}{r} \,¢ \\ \,¢ \\ +\ \,¢ \\ \hline \,¢ \end{array}$$

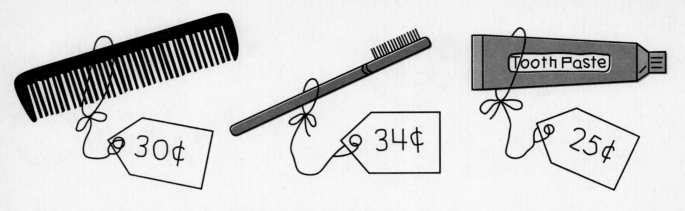

Solve each problem.

You buy a ▦▦▦ **30**¢
and a ▬▬. + **34**¢
You spend ____¢

You have   5 0¢
You buy a ▦▦▦. − **30**¢
You have left   ____¢

You buy a ▬▬ ____¢
and 🦷. + ____¢
You spend ____¢

You have   8 9¢
You buy 🦷. − ____¢
You have left   ____¢

You buy a ▦▦▦ ____¢
and 🦷. + ____¢
You spend ____¢

You have   9 7¢
You buy a ▬▬.− ____¢
You have left   ____¢

Lesson 9 Addition and Subtraction

Add.

45	53	18	40	62	76
+22	+34	+21	+30	+16	+23

32	27	50	92	42	51
+16	+40	+20	+6	+37	+24

11	40	20	35	41	10
14	12	16	22	32	20
+10	+34	+23	+40	+14	+30

Subtract.

94	66	88	73	99	44
−13	−33	−44	−23	−89	−34

59	37	86	56	80	75
−43	−12	−42	−34	−70	−52

Solve each problem.

24 frogs are in the water.

43 frogs are hopping on the land.

How many frogs in all?

$$\begin{array}{r} 24 \\ + 43 \\ \hline 67 \end{array}$$

---

60 boys were swimming at the beach.

40 girls came to swim.

How many more boys than girls?

The team shot 55 baskets.

The team missed 24 baskets.

How many baskets did the team make?

There are 44 rows of corn in a field.

There are 53 rows of corn in the other field.

How many rows of corn in all?

Lee pounded 14 posts into the ground.

Aaron pounded 23 posts.

Dale pounded 32 posts.

How many posts were pounded into the ground?

CHAPTER 5 CHECKUP

Add.

```
  44        62        40        58        71        35
 +24       +35       +30       +41       +25       +53
```

```
   5        25        41        34        52        22
   2        33        50        42        31        41
  +1       +11       + 4       +11       +14       +15
```

Subtract.

```
  25        75        86        93        67        60
 -13       -24       -53       -23       -36       -30
```

```
  49        46        58        76        82        95
 -38       -22       -43       -30       -41       -44
```

Solve each problem.

Ryan had 53¢.   ¢   Kelly had 68¢.   ¢

Corbet had 32¢.   +   ¢   She spent 44¢.   −   ¢

Ryan and Corbet   Kelly had this
  had this much.   ¢   much left.   ¢

PRE-TEST

Add.

23	16	13	37	53
+19	+17	+28	+18	+39

47	57	73	49	64
+23	+34	+18	+11	+18

25	24	26	35	51
+16	+37	+18	+16	+29

Subtract.

42	24	34	44	93
−18	−18	−17	−35	−74

86	75	66	51	22
−37	−38	−49	−27	−18

31	43	52	71	82
−18	−24	−36	−43	−66

Lesson 1 Addition and Subtraction Review

Add.

4	8	9	7	5	6
+9	+6	+8	+6	+7	+5

9	5	7	9	8	7
+6	+8	+4	+9	+7	+9

30	20	45	52	60	83
+40	+30	+23	+23	+25	+15

Subtract.

16	15	13	12	11	17
−7	−9	−4	−7	−9	−8

18	17	16	15	14	16
−9	−9	−8	−8	−7	−9

40	60	85	73	96	54
−30	−10	−23	−41	−43	−44

SPECTRUM MATHEMATICS,
Brown Book

Addition and Subtraction Review

Add.

$$\begin{array}{r} 4 \\ +8 \\ \hline \end{array} \qquad \begin{array}{r} 9 \\ +2 \\ \hline \end{array} \qquad \begin{array}{r} 5 \\ +9 \\ \hline \end{array} \qquad \begin{array}{r} 6 \\ +6 \\ \hline \end{array} \qquad \begin{array}{r} 7 \\ +5 \\ \hline \end{array} \qquad \begin{array}{r} 9 \\ +4 \\ \hline \end{array}$$

$$\begin{array}{r} 8 \\ +8 \\ \hline \end{array} \qquad \begin{array}{r} 7 \\ +6 \\ \hline \end{array} \qquad \begin{array}{r} 3 \\ +9 \\ \hline \end{array} \qquad \begin{array}{r} 7 \\ +7 \\ \hline \end{array} \qquad \begin{array}{r} 6 \\ +9 \\ \hline \end{array} \qquad \begin{array}{r} 6 \\ +5 \\ \hline \end{array}$$

$$\begin{array}{r} 40 \\ +20 \\ \hline \end{array} \qquad \begin{array}{r} 50 \\ +30 \\ \hline \end{array} \qquad \begin{array}{r} 75 \\ +20 \\ \hline \end{array} \qquad \begin{array}{r} 66 \\ +31 \\ \hline \end{array} \qquad \begin{array}{r} 47 \\ +51 \\ \hline \end{array} \qquad \begin{array}{r} 34 \\ +23 \\ \hline \end{array}$$

Subtract.

$$\begin{array}{r} 17 \\ -9 \\ \hline \end{array} \qquad \begin{array}{r} 15 \\ -6 \\ \hline \end{array} \qquad \begin{array}{r} 12 \\ -3 \\ \hline \end{array} \qquad \begin{array}{r} 13 \\ -7 \\ \hline \end{array} \qquad \begin{array}{r} 14 \\ -6 \\ \hline \end{array} \qquad \begin{array}{r} 16 \\ -8 \\ \hline \end{array}$$

$$\begin{array}{r} 15 \\ -7 \\ \hline \end{array} \qquad \begin{array}{r} 14 \\ -9 \\ \hline \end{array} \qquad \begin{array}{r} 13 \\ -6 \\ \hline \end{array} \qquad \begin{array}{r} 15 \\ -7 \\ \hline \end{array} \qquad \begin{array}{r} 12 \\ -9 \\ \hline \end{array} \qquad \begin{array}{r} 11 \\ -8 \\ \hline \end{array}$$

$$\begin{array}{r} 30 \\ -10 \\ \hline \end{array} \qquad \begin{array}{r} 50 \\ -30 \\ \hline \end{array} \qquad \begin{array}{r} 65 \\ -30 \\ \hline \end{array} \qquad \begin{array}{r} 87 \\ -34 \\ \hline \end{array} \qquad \begin{array}{r} 75 \\ -23 \\ \hline \end{array} \qquad \begin{array}{r} 66 \\ -43 \\ \hline \end{array}$$

Lesson 2 Addition (2-digit)

Add the ones.			Rename 15 as 10 + 5.	Add the tens.

$$
\begin{array}{r} 5\,6 \\ +2\,9 \\ \hline \end{array}
\qquad
\begin{array}{r} 6 \\ +9 \\ \hline 15 \end{array} \text{ or } 10 + 5
\qquad\Longrightarrow\qquad
\begin{array}{r} 1 \\ 5\,6 \\ +2\,9 \\ \hline 5 \end{array}
\qquad\Longrightarrow\qquad
\begin{array}{r} 1 \\ 5\,6 \\ +2\,9 \\ \hline 8\,5 \end{array}
$$

Add the ones.			Rename 12 as 10 + 2.	Add the tens.

$$
\begin{array}{r} 4\,7 \\ +3\,5 \\ \hline \end{array}
\qquad
\begin{array}{r} 7 \\ +5 \\ \hline 12 \end{array} \text{ or } 10 + 2
\qquad
\begin{array}{r} 1 \\ 4\,7 \\ +3\,5 \\ \hline 2 \end{array}
\qquad
\begin{array}{r} 1 \\ 4\,7 \\ +3\,5 \\ \hline 8\,2 \end{array}
$$

Add.

$$
\begin{array}{r} 4\,5 \\ +2\,8 \\ \hline 7\,3 \end{array}
\qquad
\begin{array}{r} 1\,3 \\ +1\,9 \\ \hline 3\,2 \end{array}
\qquad
\begin{array}{r} 4\,8 \\ +3\,5 \\ \hline \end{array}
\qquad
\begin{array}{r} 6\,9 \\ +1\,8 \\ \hline \end{array}
\qquad
\begin{array}{r} 5\,4 \\ +3\,9 \\ \hline \end{array}
$$

$$
\begin{array}{r} 4\,4 \\ +1\,7 \\ \hline \end{array}
\qquad
\begin{array}{r} 3\,7 \\ +1\,8 \\ \hline \end{array}
\qquad
\begin{array}{r} 2\,8 \\ +3\,6 \\ \hline \end{array}
\qquad
\begin{array}{r} 7\,3 \\ +1\,8 \\ \hline \end{array}
\qquad
\begin{array}{r} 6\,6 \\ +2\,9 \\ \hline \end{array}
$$

$$
\begin{array}{r} 5\,2 \\ +3\,9 \\ \hline \end{array}
\qquad
\begin{array}{r} 3\,8 \\ +4\,7 \\ \hline \end{array}
\qquad
\begin{array}{r} 6\,4 \\ +1\,8 \\ \hline \end{array}
\qquad
\begin{array}{r} 2\,9 \\ +4\,5 \\ \hline \end{array}
\qquad
\begin{array}{r} 7\,5 \\ +1\,7 \\ \hline \end{array}
$$

Addition (2-digit)

Add the ones. Rename 11 as 10 + 1. **Add the tens.**

```
  3 8          8              1              1
 +4 3         +3             3 8            3 8
             ────          +4 3           +4 3
             1 1  or  10 + 1 ──→ 1         8 1
```

Add.

```
  1 7          2 6           4 7           6 8           3 7
 +3 4         +4 7          +3 5          +2 4          +2 8
 ────
  5 1
```

```
  2 9          5 8           6 9           7 8           1 9
 +4 8         +2 7          +1 7          +1 3          +4 4
```

```
  5 5          2 7           3 9           5 7           3 8
 +2 8         +3 5          +5 2          +2 7          +3 6
```

```
  4 9          6 5           2 3           6 4           4 6
 +4 3         +1 8          +1 8          +1 8          +3 9
```

```
  5 4          3 8           6 6           2 8           1 9
 +2 7         +4 4          +2 6          +3 4          +5 6
```

Lesson 3   Addition (2-digit)

Add the ones.   Rename 12 as 10 + 2.   **Add the tens.**

```
  6 4        4                        1                            1
 +2 8       +8                       6 4                          6 4
            ———                     +2 8             ⇒           +2 8
            12  or  10 + 2 ————→ 2                              9 2
```

Add.

```
  2 8        3 4        2 5        4 6        5 4
 +1 9       +4 9       +1 6       +2 9       +3 9
 ————
 4 7
```

```
  1 6        6 4        5 8        3 9        3 4
 +3 9       +2 8       +2 4       +1 7       +1 9
```

```
  5 7        1 4        3 7        6 1        2 9
 +3 9       +4 8       +3 9       +1 9       +4 4
```

```
  1 7        3 9        4 4        2 5        1 8
 +3 5       +1 4       +3 7       +4 9       +1 8
```

```
  2 6        3 9        1 4        6 5        5 9
 +4 8       +2 7       +2 7       +2 5       +1 8
```

SPECTRUM MATHEMATICS,
Brown Book

Solve each problem.

16 boys ride their bikes to school.

18 girls ride their bikes to school.

How many bikes are ridden to school?

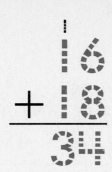

$$\begin{array}{r} 16 \\ + 18 \\ \hline 34 \end{array}$$

Dad reads 26 pages.

Mike reads 37 pages.

How many pages did Dad and Mike read?

Tiffany counts 46 stars.

Mike counts 39 stars.

How many stars did they count?

Mom has 29 golf balls.

Dad has 43 golf balls.

How many golf balls do they have?

Vicki ran in 26 races.

Kay ran in 14 races.

How many races did they run?

Lesson 4 Addition (2-digit)

Add.

3 6 +5 5	1 4 +2 8	5 7 +3 8	4 4 +4 8	3 3 +2 9
2 3 +1 8	2 7 +2 7	6 8 +2 5	2 3 +1 9	4 2 +1 9
5 6 +2 8	4 9 +2 7	3 8 +4 9	3 6 +1 8	4 9 +2 4
1 8 +5 4	5 1 +3 9	7 4 +1 7	3 5 +2 8	5 2 +1 9
4 8 +2 6	2 5 +2 8	3 9 +3 3	2 9 +4 4	5 4 +2 7

SPECTRUM MATHEMATICS,
Brown Book

Solve each problem.

Simon sees 36 birds flying.

Julie sees 28 birds flying.

How many birds do they see flying?

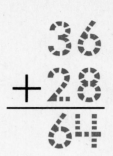

Brandon ran the race in 35 seconds.

Ryan ran the race in 28 seconds.

How many seconds did they run?

Nicole has 63 nickels.

Meagan has 29 nickels.

How many nickels do they have?

Pam sees 48 monkeys at the zoo.

Katie sees 35 different monkeys.

How many monkeys did they see?

There are 29 steers in one pen.

There are 47 steers in the other pen.

How many steers in all?

Lesson 5 Subtraction (2-digit)

Rename 53 as 4 tens and
13 ones.

$$\begin{array}{r} {}^{4}5{}^{13}3 \\ -2\ 6 \end{array}$$

Subtract the ones.

$$\begin{array}{r} {}^{4}5{}^{13}3 \\ -2\ 6 \\ \hline 7 \end{array}$$

Subtract the tens.

$$\begin{array}{r} {}^{4}5{}^{13}3 \\ -2\ 6 \\ \hline 2\ 7 \end{array}$$

Rename 45 as 3 tens and
15 ones.

$$\begin{array}{r} {}^{3}4{}^{15}5 \\ -1\ 8 \end{array}$$

Subtract the ones.

$$\begin{array}{r} {}^{3}4{}^{15}5 \\ -1\ 8 \\ \hline 7 \end{array}$$

Subtract the tens.

$$\begin{array}{r} {}^{3}4{}^{15}5 \\ -1\ 8 \\ \hline 2\ 7 \end{array}$$

Subtract.

$$\begin{array}{r} {}^{5}6{}^{13}3 \\ -2\ 8 \\ \hline 35 \end{array} \qquad \begin{array}{r} {}^{6}7{}^{14}4 \\ -3\ 9 \\ \hline 35 \end{array} \qquad \begin{array}{r} 4\ 7 \\ -2\ 8 \\ \hline \end{array} \qquad \begin{array}{r} 5\ 2 \\ -2\ 6 \\ \hline \end{array} \qquad \begin{array}{r} 6\ 4 \\ -3\ 6 \\ \hline \end{array}$$

$$\begin{array}{r} 8\ 4 \\ -4\ 7 \\ \hline \end{array} \qquad \begin{array}{r} 9\ 3 \\ -5\ 6 \\ \hline \end{array} \qquad \begin{array}{r} 7\ 1 \\ -2\ 3 \\ \hline \end{array} \qquad \begin{array}{r} 2\ 6 \\ -1\ 8 \\ \hline \end{array} \qquad \begin{array}{r} 6\ 7 \\ -4\ 8 \\ \hline \end{array}$$

$$\begin{array}{r} 4\ 4 \\ -2\ 8 \\ \hline \end{array} \qquad \begin{array}{r} 5\ 3 \\ -3\ 7 \\ \hline \end{array} \qquad \begin{array}{r} 8\ 2 \\ -4\ 6 \\ \hline \end{array} \qquad \begin{array}{r} 9\ 4 \\ -6\ 6 \\ \hline \end{array} \qquad \begin{array}{r} 5\ 5 \\ -3\ 9 \\ \hline \end{array}$$

$$\begin{array}{r} 8\ 6 \\ -5\ 8 \\ \hline \end{array} \qquad \begin{array}{r} 3\ 4 \\ -1\ 8 \\ \hline \end{array} \qquad \begin{array}{r} 5\ 4 \\ -2\ 9 \\ \hline \end{array} \qquad \begin{array}{r} 7\ 3 \\ -5\ 9 \\ \hline \end{array} \qquad \begin{array}{r} 8\ 6 \\ -6\ 9 \\ \hline \end{array}$$

Subtraction (2-digit)

Rename 73 as 6 tens and 13 ones.

```
      6 13
 7 3    7 3
-4 8  -4 8
```

Subtract the ones.

```
      6 13
       7̶ 3
      -4 8
         5
```

Subtract the tens.

```
      6 13
       7̶ 3
      -4 8
       2 5
```

Subtract.

```
  5 13
  6 3      8 3      7 4      9 4      6 2
 -4 8     -4 5     -2 9     -4 8     -2 5
  1 5
```

```
  4 5      3 3      2 4      8 6      7 2
 -2 7     -2 4     -1 8     -3 7     -4 8
```

```
  3 6      2 6      4 3      6 3      9 3
 -1 7     -1 8     -1 9     -4 8     -1 8
```

```
  8 2      7 3      9 5      5 7      4 1
 -2 6     -2 8     -6 9     -3 8     -2 5
```

```
  5 4      6 1      9 1      8 1      3 2
 -1 8     -3 4     -3 7     -4 4     -1 5
```

SPECTRUM MATHEMATICS,
Brown Book

Lesson 6   Subtraction (2-digit)

Rename 61 as 5 tens and 11 ones.

$$\begin{array}{r} 6\ 1 \\ -4\ 3 \\ \hline \end{array}$$

$$\begin{array}{r} 5\ 11 \\ 6\ \not{1} \\ -4\ 3 \\ \hline \end{array}$$

Subtract the ones.

$$\begin{array}{r} 5\ 11 \\ 6\ \not{1} \\ -4\ 3 \\ \hline 8 \end{array}$$

Subtract the tens.

$$\begin{array}{r} 5\ 11 \\ 6\ \not{1} \\ -4\ 3 \\ \hline 1\ 8 \end{array}$$

Subtract.

$$\begin{array}{r} 3\ 17 \\ \not{4}\ \not{7} \\ -2\ 8 \\ \hline 1\ 9 \end{array} \qquad \begin{array}{r} 7\ 3 \\ -4\ 8 \\ \hline \end{array} \qquad \begin{array}{r} 8\ 4 \\ -6\ 6 \\ \hline \end{array} \qquad \begin{array}{r} 9\ 5 \\ -1\ 8 \\ \hline \end{array} \qquad \begin{array}{r} 6\ 4 \\ -2\ 9 \\ \hline \end{array}$$

$$\begin{array}{r} 5\ 6 \\ -3\ 8 \\ \hline \end{array} \qquad \begin{array}{r} 3\ 1 \\ -1\ 5 \\ \hline \end{array} \qquad \begin{array}{r} 2\ 5 \\ -1\ 7 \\ \hline \end{array} \qquad \begin{array}{r} 3\ 3 \\ -1\ 9 \\ \hline \end{array} \qquad \begin{array}{r} 4\ 6 \\ -2\ 9 \\ \hline \end{array}$$

$$\begin{array}{r} 9\ 3 \\ -6\ 4 \\ \hline \end{array} \qquad \begin{array}{r} 8\ 2 \\ -5\ 5 \\ \hline \end{array} \qquad \begin{array}{r} 7\ 2 \\ -1\ 4 \\ \hline \end{array} \qquad \begin{array}{r} 4\ 5 \\ -2\ 8 \\ \hline \end{array} \qquad \begin{array}{r} 6\ 1 \\ -2\ 3 \\ \hline \end{array}$$

$$\begin{array}{r} 5\ 1 \\ -4\ 4 \\ \hline \end{array} \qquad \begin{array}{r} 6\ 2 \\ -4\ 8 \\ \hline \end{array} \qquad \begin{array}{r} 3\ 7 \\ -1\ 9 \\ \hline \end{array} \qquad \begin{array}{r} 5\ 0 \\ -3\ 2 \\ \hline \end{array} \qquad \begin{array}{r} 8\ 3 \\ -4\ 7 \\ \hline \end{array}$$

$$\begin{array}{r} 9\ 2 \\ -7\ 3 \\ \hline \end{array} \qquad \begin{array}{r} 8\ 2 \\ -7\ 5 \\ \hline \end{array} \qquad \begin{array}{r} 7\ 6 \\ -3\ 8 \\ \hline \end{array} \qquad \begin{array}{r} 4\ 7 \\ -2\ 9 \\ \hline \end{array} \qquad \begin{array}{r} 7\ 4 \\ -3\ 9 \\ \hline \end{array}$$

Solve each problem.

Dad cooks 23 potatoes.

He uses 19 potatoes in the potato salad.

How many potatoes are left?

$$\begin{array}{r} \overset{1}{\cancel{2}}\overset{13}{\cancel{3}} \\ -19 \\ \hline 4 \end{array}$$

Susan draws 32 butterflies.

She colors 15 of them brown.

How many does she have left to color?

A book has 66 pages.

Pedro reads 39 pages.

How many pages are left to read?

Jesse picks up 34 seashells.

He puts 15 of them in a box.

How many does he have left?

Beth buys 72 sheets of paper.

She uses 44 sheets for her schoolwork.

How many sheets of paper are left?

Lesson 7   Subtraction

Subtract.

8 5 −1 6	9 3 −4 8	7 2 −3 5	6 3 −2 7	4 3 −3 8
5 6 −2 9	7 5 −4 9	8 4 −3 8	9 1 −6 5	3 7 −1 8
2 1 −1 4	3 5 −1 8	4 2 −2 9	7 2 −4 7	8 1 −5 4
6 4 −3 8	5 3 −2 8	9 4 −5 7	4 8 −3 9	2 3 −1 8
7 4 −5 8	8 3 −3 6	6 2 −2 6	5 4 −2 8	3 2 −1 7

Solve each problem.

Scott has 40 pennies.

Tracy has 45 pennies.

How many pennies in all?

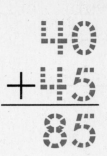

Mom puts 36 nails in a box.

Edna takes 18 nails out of the box.

How many nails are left in the box?

Liz buys 57 apples and oranges.

29 are oranges.

How many are apples?

Tony can jump a rope 84 times.

Curt can jump a rope 69 times.

How many more times can Tony jump?

The team scored 74 points.

Michelle scored 37 of the points.

How many points did the rest of the team score?

Lesson 8 Addition and Subtraction (2-digit)

Add.

6 4 +2 9	3 7 +4 6	2 4 +1 9	7 1 +1 9	4 9 +1 8
2 7 +4 4	3 3 +1 8	2 8 +2 5	5 9 +1 6	3 4 +4 8
4 3 +2 9	2 6 +4 5	7 2 +1 9	6 9 +1 5	1 8 +3 9

Subtract.

7 6 −4 8	6 7 −5 9	8 8 −6 9	9 3 −4 8	4 5 −2 7
8 4 −1 6	9 5 −2 7	3 6 −1 8	6 3 −2 8	7 2 −4 9
9 1 −3 2	7 2 −4 5	6 2 −1 8	5 4 −3 6	3 3 −1 9

Solve each problem.

Mr. Smith milks 64 🐄 .

Mrs. Jones milks 29 🐄.

How many more 🐄 does Mr. Smith milk than Mrs. Jones?

$$\begin{array}{r} \overset{5}{\cancel{6}}\overset{14}{\cancel{4}} \\ -29 \\ \hline 35 \end{array}$$

There are 13 girls playing ⚾ .

18 more girls join in to play.

How many girls are playing ⚾ ?

Erin served the ⚽ 34 times.

Jeff served the ⚽ 19 times.

How many more times did Erin serve?

---

62 red 🌹 grew in the garden.

29 yellow 🌹 grew there too.

How many 🌹 grew in the garden?

Jon has 62 🔨 .

He hammers 45 🔨 into the board.

How many 🔨 does Jon have left?

CHAPTER 6 CHECKUP

Add.

2 4	5 6	4 9	6 2	3 9
+1 8	+2 7	+2 6	+1 9	+1 8

2 8	7 3	6 4	5 9	1 3
+3 4	+1 9	+1 8	+3 3	+1 8

Subtract.

5 3	7 6	9 7	6 2	4 4
−2 7	−4 7	−7 8	−3 8	−2 6

8 4	3 8	2 5	8 2	9 6
−3 9	−2 9	−1 8	−4 8	−7 9

Solve each problem.

There are 26 pieces of chalk on the chalkboard.

18 pieces fall on the floor.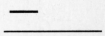

How many pieces are still on the chalkboard?

_____

Jason did 26 pages of homework.

Beth did 36 pages of homework.

How many pages of homework did they do in all?

SPECTRUM MATHEMATICS,
Brown Book

PRE-TEST

Write the numerals.

5 hundreds 3 tens 2 ones	8 hundreds 4 tens 1 one
_____	_____
4 hundreds 8 tens 6 ones	3 hundreds 7 tens 8 ones
_____	_____

Add.

```
  300        600        200        500
 +100       +300       +300       +200
```

```
  569        432        215        626
 +120       +246       +442       + 13
```

Subtract.

```
  400        800        600        300
 -300       -100       -400       -200
```

```
  846        768        346        585
 -321       -616       - 32       -261
```

Lesson 1   Numbers 100 Through 199

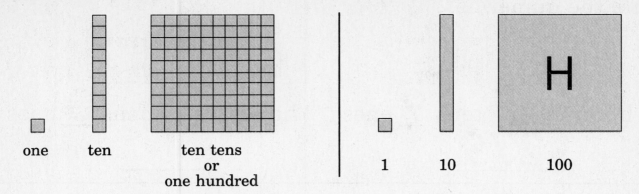

one   ten   ten tens
                        or
                   one hundred

1   10   100

Write the numerals.

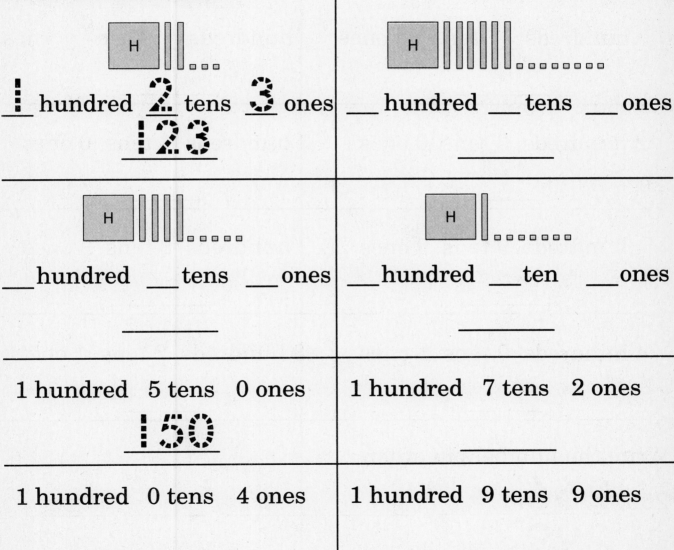

__1__ hundred __2__ tens __3__ ones

__123__

___ hundred ___ tens ___ ones

_____

___ hundred ___ tens ___ ones

_____

___ hundred ___ ten ___ ones

_____

1 hundred 5 tens   0 ones

__150__

1 hundred 7 tens   2 ones

_____

1 hundred 0 tens   4 ones

_____

1 hundred 9 tens   9 ones

_____

Lesson 2 Numbers 200 Through 499
Write the numerals.

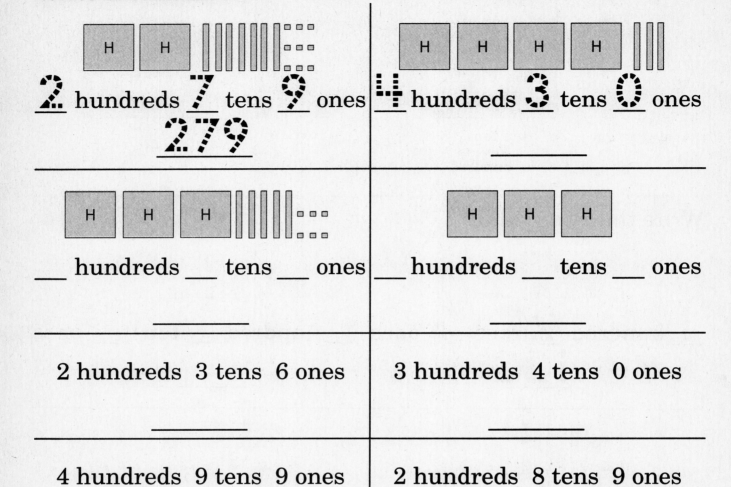

2 hundreds 7 tens 9 ones

__279__

_____

4 hundreds 3 tens 0 ones

_____

_____

___ hundreds ___ tens ___ ones

_____

_____

___ hundreds ___ tens ___ ones

_____

_____

2 hundreds 3 tens 6 ones

_____

3 hundreds 4 tens 0 ones

_____

4 hundreds 9 tens 9 ones

_____

2 hundreds 8 tens 9 ones

_____

4 hundreds 0 tens 4 ones

_____

3 hundreds 2 tens 1 one

_____

Write the numbers in order.

265, __266__, _____ , _____ , _____ , _____ , _____

398, __399__, _____ , _____ , _____ , _____ , _____

Lesson 3   Numbers 500 Through 799
Write the numerals.

5 hundreds **2** tens **0** ones

_____

___ hundreds ___ tens ___ ones

_____

6 hundreds 2 tens 1 one

_____

7 hundreds 1 ten 4 ones

_____

5 hundreds 5 tens 3 ones

_____

6 hundreds 9 tens 7 ones

_____

6 hundreds 7 tens 8 ones

_____

7 hundreds 3 tens 2 ones

_____

7 hundreds 6 tens 5 ones

_____

5 hundreds 8 tens 3 ones

_____

6 hundreds 1 ten 0 ones

_____

7 hundreds 7 tens 6 ones

_____

7 hundreds 9 tens 9 ones

_____

5 hundreds 8 tens 8 ones

_____

Lesson 4 Numbers 800 Through 999

Write the numerals.

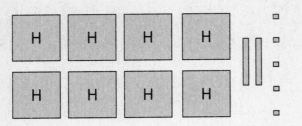 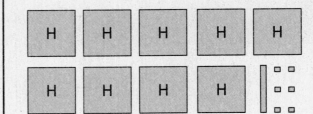

8 hundreds **2** tens **5** ones   ___ hundreds ___ ten ___ ones

_____   _____

9 hundreds 2 tens 8 ones   8 hundreds 4 tens 2 ones

_____   _____

8 hundreds 9 tens 2 ones   9 hundreds 0 tens 3 ones

_____   _____

9 hundreds 7 tens 5 ones   8 hundreds 4 tens 0 ones

_____   _____

Count by hundreds to complete the row.

100, **200**, _____, _____, _____, _____, _____, _____ ,900

Count by tens to complete the row.

850, 860, _____, _____, _____, _____, _____, _____, _____

Lesson 5 Numbers 100 Through 999
Write the numerals.

8 hundreds 6 tens 4 ones	5 hundreds 3 tens 8 ones
_____	_____
3 hundreds 1 ten 5 ones	9 hundreds 8 tens 3 ones
_____	_____
1 hundred 0 tens 1 one	4 hundreds 2 tens 7 ones
_____	_____

Start at 780.
Connect the dots in order.

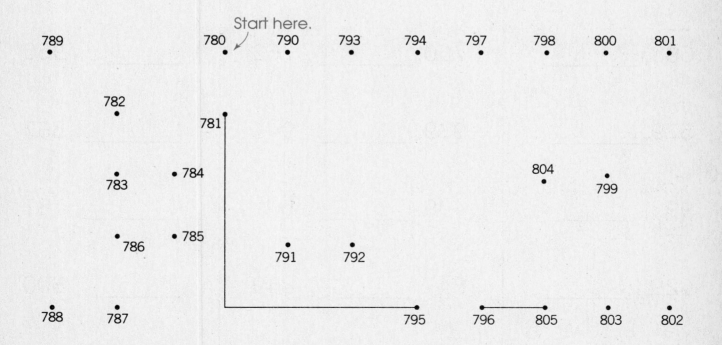

Numbers 100 Through 999

Complete.

After	_Between_	_Before_
419, __420__	818, __819__, 820	__770__, 771
301, _____	324, _____, 326	_____, 346
143, _____	606, _____, 608	_____, 160
854, _____	255, _____, 257	_____, 200
209, _____	172, _____, 174	_____, 423
688, _____	760, _____, 762	_____, 950
579, _____	939, _____, 941	_____, 667
993, _____	499, _____, 501	_____, 181
629, _____	847, _____, 849	_____, 800
799, _____	583, _____, 585	_____, 595

Lesson 6 Adding Hundreds

NAME _____

5 hundreds	5 0 0	4 hundreds	4 0 0
+3 hundreds	+3 0 0	+5 hundreds	+5 0 0
8 hundreds	8 0 0	9 hundreds	900

Add.

3 hundreds	3 0 0	6 hundreds	6 0 0
+1 hundred	+1 0 0	+2 hundreds	+2 0 0
4 hundreds	400	hundreds	

2 0 0	1 0 0	6 0 0	4 0 0
+2 0 0	+7 0 0	+3 0 0	+5 0 0

3 0 0	8 0 0	4 0 0	7 0 0
+4 0 0	+1 0 0	+4 0 0	+2 0 0

5 0 0	1 0 0	5 0 0	3 0 0
+1 0 0	+6 0 0	+2 0 0	+2 0 0

3 0 0	4 0 0	3 0 0	2 0 0
+3 0 0	+2 0 0	+5 0 0	+1 0 0

SPECTRUM MATHEMATICS,
Brown Book

Solve each problem.

Ria packed 300 boxes.

Melody packed 200 boxes.

How many boxes did Ria and Melody pack?

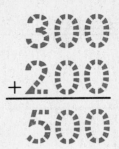

$$\begin{array}{r} 300 \\ +200 \\ \hline 500 \end{array}$$

Santo typed 500 letters.

Hale typed 400 letters.

How many letters did they type?

Paula used 100 paper clips.

Heidi used 600 paper clips.

How many paper clips did they use?

The grocery store sold 400 red apples.

The grocery store also sold 100 yellow apples.

How many apples did the store sell in all?

Miles worked 200 days.

Julia worked 500 days.

How many days did they work?

Lesson 7 Addition (3-digit)

```
  2 4 5              2 4 5              2 4 5
+ 2 5 3            + 2 5 3            + 2 5 3
      8                9 8              4 9 8
```

Add.

```
  7 4 5                      6 2 3
+   2 3                    + 1 5 6
```

Add the ones.
Add the tens.
Add the hundreds.

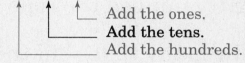

Add the ones.
Add the tens.
Add the hundreds.

```
  4 1 5        5 6 6        3 7 3        1 6 0
+ 3 4 2        + 3 3      + 2 2 1      + 3 3 4
```

```
  8 3 5        6 4 2        2 8 7        7 2 3
+   4 2      + 2 5 1      + 4 1 2      +   4 5
```

```
  1 3 3        4 5 4        3 1 4        6 5 4
+ 5 2 2      + 3 2 4      + 6 0 2      + 2 3 5
```

Solve each problem.

Gene collected 342 rocks.

Ashley collected 201 rocks.

How many rocks did they collect?

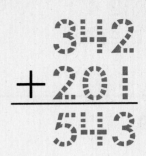

Tina jumped the rope 403 times.

Henry jumped the rope 426 times.

How many times did they jump?

There are 210 people wearing blue hats.

There are 432 people wearing red hats.

How many hats in all?

Asta used 135 paper plates.

Jordan used 143 paper plates.

How many paper plates did they use in all?

Aunt Mary had 536 dollars.

Uncle Lewis had 423 dollars.

How many dollars did they have in all?

Lesson 8 Addition (3-digit)

Add.

340 +225 **565**	754 + 32 **786**	826 + 3	632 +322
198 +200	456 + 31	541 +333	273 +415
900 + 34	847 +131	721 +176	402 +383
156 +423	644 +251	215 +542	372 +417
518 +351	783 + 5	684 + 14	710 +260

Solve each problem.

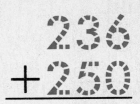

There are 236 boys in school.

There are 250 girls in school.

How many boys and girls are
in school?

Adam saw 131 cars.

Travis saw 268 trucks.

How many cars and trucks did they
see in all?

Ben has 427 pennies.

Trevor has 370 pennies.

How many pennies do they
have in all?

There are 582 red apples.

There are 206 yellow apples.

How many apples are there in all?

Ann found 122 shells.

Pedro found 76 shells.

How many shells did they find?

Lesson 9 Subtracting Hundreds

8 hundreds	8 0 0		6 hundreds	6 0 0
−3 hundreds	−3 0 0		−2 hundreds	−2 0 0
5 hundreds	5 0 0		4 hundreds	4 0 0

Subtract.

9 hundreds	9 0 0		3 hundreds	3 0 0
−7 hundreds	−7 0 0		−1 hundred	−1 0 0
2 hundreds	2 0 0		hundreds	

7 0 0	5 0 0	9 0 0	8 0 0
−3 0 0	−4 0 0	−4 0 0	−5 0 0

6 0 0	3 0 0	5 0 0	4 0 0
−5 0 0	−2 0 0	−1 0 0	−2 0 0

9 0 0	8 0 0	6 0 0	5 0 0
−1 0 0	−4 0 0	−2 0 0	−3 0 0

4 0 0	7 0 0	8 0 0	9 0 0
−1 0 0	−6 0 0	−2 0 0	−6 0 0

Solve each problem.

There were 400 apples in a box.

Jesse took 100 apples from the box.

How many apples are still in the box?

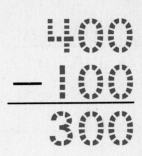

Ethan bought 300 golf balls.

He gave Irene 200 golf balls.

How many golf balls does he have left?

The black horse ran 900 feet.

The brown horse ran 700 feet.

How many more feet did the black horse run?

The paint store has 800 gallons of paint.

It sells 300 gallons of paint.

How many gallons of paint are left?

There are 700 children.

There are 200 boys.

How many girls are there?

Lesson 10 Subtraction (3-digit)

Subtract the ones.

```
  746
 -424
    2
```

Subtract the tens.

```
  746
 -424
   22
```

Subtract the hundreds.

```
  746
 -424
  322
```

Subtract.

```
  879
 - 46
```

833

— Subtract the ones.
Subtract the tens.
— Subtract the hundreds.

```
  586
 -142
```

— Subtract the ones.
Subtract the tens.
— Subtract the hundreds.

```
  635
 -423
```

```
  478
 -241
```

```
  338
 - 27
```

```
  957
 -734
```

```
  297
 -145
```

```
  846
 -325
```

```
  769
 -514
```

```
  653
 -142
```

```
  569
 -333
```

```
  365
 -213
```

```
  818
 -618
```

```
  936
 -424
```

Solve each problem.

The grocery store buys 568 cans of beans.

It sells 345 cans of beans.

How many cans of beans are left?

$$\begin{array}{r} 568 \\ -\ 345 \\ \hline 223 \end{array}$$

The cooler holds 732 gallons of milk.

It has 412 gallons of milk in it.

How many more gallons of milk will it take to fill the cooler?

Ann does 635 push-ups

Carl does 421 push-ups.

How many more push-ups does Ann do?

Kurt has 386 pennies.

Neal has 32 pennies.

How many more pennies does Kurt have?

It takes 874 nails to build a tree house.

Jillian has 532 nails.

How many more nails does she need?

Lesson 11 Subtraction (3-digit)

Subtract.

856 −352 **504**	432 − 21 **411**	598 −416	769 −345
319 − 6	954 −731	275 − 3	643 −313
775 −261	834 − 12	942 −111	478 −324
562 −431	444 −212	385 −152	754 − 3
868 −234	943 −843	689 −417	577 − 37

Solve each problem.

There were 787 bales of hay.

Glenda fed the cows 535 bales.

How many bales of hay are left?

$$\begin{array}{r} 787 \\ -535 \\ \hline 252 \end{array}$$

There are 673 bolts in a box.

Maria took 341 bolts out of the box.

How many bolts are left in the box?

The secretary typed 459 letters.

138 of the letters were mailed.

How many letters are left?

Vikas had 569 dollars.

He spent 203 dollars.

How many dollars does he have left?

There are 342 riding horses in the rodeo.

There are 132 bucking horses in the rodeo.

How many more riding horses are there?

CHAPTER 7 CHECKUP

Write the numerals.

1 hundred 0 tens 5 ones	9 hundreds 6 tens 4 ones
_____	_____
6 hundreds 1 ten 8 ones	3 hundreds 2 tens 7 ones
_____	_____
3 hundreds 7 tens 1 one	7 hundreds 1 ten 9 ones
_____	_____

Write the numbers in order.

497, 498, _____ , _____ , _____

Count by tens. Complete the row.

460, _____ , _____ , _____ , *500*

Add.

$$\begin{array}{r} 3\,0\,0 \\ +5\,0\,0 \\ \hline \end{array} \qquad \begin{array}{r} 4\,0\,0 \\ +4\,0\,0 \\ \hline \end{array} \qquad \begin{array}{r} 4\,9\,7 \\ +1\,0\,0 \\ \hline \end{array} \qquad \begin{array}{r} 2\,0\,3 \\ +\ \ 4\,6 \\ \hline \end{array}$$

Add.

```
  124        520        739        861
 +323       +407       +150       +  6
```

Subtract.

```
  900        800        974        508
 -600       -200       -564       -  7
```

```
  728        657        894        596
 -326       - 45       -464       -352
```

Solve each problem.

There are 275 nails in a box.

123 nails are taken out of the box.

How many nails are still in the box?

_____

Colin peeled 212 apples.

Anna peeled 84 apples.

How many apples did they peel in all?

CHECKUP   Chapters 1–4
Complete.

4 tens 6 ones = _____   8 tens 0 ones = _____

Write the next three numbers.

26, 27, 28, _____,_____,_____

91, 92, 93, _____,_____,_____

Count by 10.

10, 20, 30, _____,_____,_____,_____

Add.

7	5	3	8	0
+2	+0	+4	+2	+3

8	9	4	2	9
+4	+9	+7	+9	+7

5	8	7	6	7
+8	+9	+8	+6	+7

Subtract.

9	4	8	6	7
−6	−2	−5	−1	−5

1 0	1 5	1 3	1 1	1 7
− 2	− 7	− 5	− 6	− 8

1 2	1 8	1 3	1 5	1 6
− 7	− 9	− 9	− 6	− 8

How long is each object?

Use a centimeter ruler.

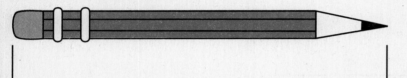

Use an inch ruler.

_____ centimeters

_____ inches

Ring the fraction that tells how much is blue.

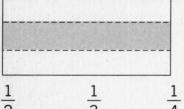

$\frac{1}{2}$ $\qquad$ $\frac{1}{3}$ $\qquad$ $\frac{1}{4}$

$\frac{1}{2}$ $\qquad$ $\frac{1}{3}$ $\qquad$ $\frac{1}{4}$

$\frac{1}{2}$ $\qquad$ $\frac{1}{3}$ $\qquad$ $\frac{1}{4}$

Write the time for each clock.

6:00

_____ : _____

_____ : _____

_____ : _____

FINAL CHECKUP Chapters 1–7

Add.

8 +2	3 +4	9 +6	8 +8	6 +7	8 +9

30 +50	41 +28	93 + 4	3 2 +3	10 20 +30	12 24 +51

38 +46	25 +28	47 +44	200 +500	774 +123	291 +408

Subtract.

9 − 6	7 − 3	10 − 5	12 − 3	17 − 9	15 − 8

60 −10	39 −21	82 −72	56 −40	96 −15	47 −31

87 −38	50 −22	72 −58	175 − 62	384 −270	875 −641

Complete.

   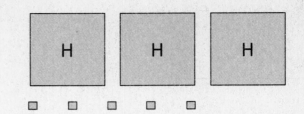

5 tens 2 ones = _____   3 hundreds 0 tens 5 ones = _____

8 tens 9 ones = _____   7 hundreds 3 tens 6 ones = _____

6 tens 0 ones = _____   9 hundreds 5 tens 8 ones = _____

Write the next three numbers.

47, 48, 49, _____, _____, _____

293, 294, 295, _____, _____, _____

Count by 10.

40, 50, 60, _____, _____, _____

500, 510, 520, _____, _____, _____

FINAL CHECKUP (Continued)

How long is each object?

Use a centimeter ruler.

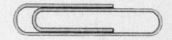

_____ centimeters

_____ centimeters

Use an inch ruler.

_____ inch

_____ inches

Ring the fraction that tells how much is blue.

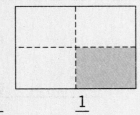

$\frac{1}{2}$ $\frac{1}{3}$ $\frac{1}{4}$

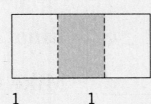

$\frac{1}{2}$ $\frac{1}{3}$ $\frac{1}{4}$

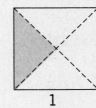

$\frac{1}{2}$ $\frac{1}{3}$ $\frac{1}{4}$

Write the time for each clock.

_____ : _____

_____ : _____

_____ : _____

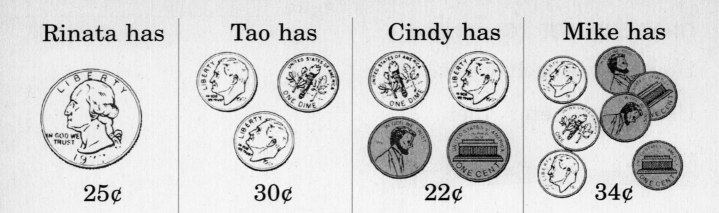

Rinata has	Tao has	Cindy has	Mike has
25¢	30¢	22¢	34¢

Solve each problem.

Rinata has	**25**¢	Mike has	**34**¢
Cindy has	**−22**¢	Tao has	**+30**¢
Rinata has this much more.	**3**¢	Together they have this much.	**64**¢

Mike has	¢	Rinata has	¢
Tao has	− ¢	Mike has	+ ¢
Mike has this much more.	¢	Together they have this much.	¢

Mike has	¢	Cindy has	¢
Rinata has	− ¢	Tao has	+ ¢
Mike has this much more.	¢	Together they have this much.	¢

SPECTRUM MATHEMATICS,
Brown Book

CHAPTER 1   CUMULATIVE REVIEW

Add.

2 +1	0 +4	8 +1	4 +3	6 +4	3 +3
8 +2	3 +6	2 +4	1 +3	6 +2	5 +4
5 +5	2 +3	3 +7	1 +5	7 +0	5 +2

Subtract.

8 −5	9 −2	6 −6	4 −3	1 −0	10 −5
6 −4	10 −9	5 −2	8 −7	9 −1	6 −3
10 −6	7 −3	8 −4	10 −8	7 −5	9 −6

CHAPTER 2 CUMULATIVE REVIEW

Complete.

7 tens 2 ones	=	_____
2 tens 4 ones	=	_____
6 tens 1 one	=	_____
3 tens 5 ones	=	_____
8 tens	=	_____
5 tens 6 ones	=	_____

9 tens 3 ones	=	_____
1 ten 8 ones	=	_____
4 tens	=	_____
6 tens 6 ones	=	_____
8 tens 4 ones	=	_____
7 tens 1 one	=	_____

Name the next four numbers.

2, 3, 4, ___, ___, ___, ___

45, 46, 47, _____, _____, _____, _____

66, 67, 68, _____, _____, _____, _____

93, 94, 95, _____, _____, _____, _____

78, 79, 80, _____, _____, _____, _____

50, 51, 52, _____, _____, _____, _____

SPECTRUM MATHEMATICS,
Brown Book

CHAPTER 3   CUMULATIVE REVIEW

Add.

7	9	6	8	9	7
+8	+5	+7	+8	+6	+7

5	7	9	5	8	9
+6	+7	+7	+8	+6	+9

Subtract.

1 2	1 4	1 3	1 8	1 5	1 6
− 9	− 8	− 4	− 9	− 7	− 9

1 7	1 5	1 2	1 6	1 3	1 4
− 9	− 8	− 4	− 8	− 8	− 7

Solve.

There are 13 ducks swimming.

There are 8 ducks flying.

How many more ducks are swimming than flying?

CHAPTER 4 CUMULATIVE REVIEW

How long is each object?

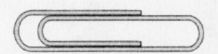

____ centimeters

____ centimeters

____ inches

____ inches

Write the time for each clock.

___ : ____

___ : ____

___ : ____

Ring the fraction that tells how much is blue.

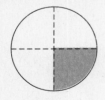

$\frac{1}{2}$ $\frac{1}{3}$ $\frac{1}{4}$

$\frac{1}{2}$ $\frac{1}{3}$ $\frac{1}{4}$

$\frac{1}{2}$ $\frac{1}{3}$ $\frac{1}{4}$

CHAPTER 5 CUMULATIVE REVIEW

Add.

3 1	6 2	4 7	5 6	2 8	7 3
+4 5	+2 6	+3 1	+2 0	+6 1	+1 5

2 0	6 3	2 1	5 2	2 2	1 2
3 0	1 4	3 3	1 6	1 3	3 0
+4 0	+ 2	+4 2	+1 1	+4 0	+2 6

Subtract.

8 3	5 0	9 5	6 9	8 2	7 8
−2 3	−3 0	−2 2	−3 8	−5 1	−4 3

4 0	2 7	3 8	8 8	7 2	6 3
−1 0	−1 3	−2 6	−4 0	−3 1	−2 2

Solve each problem.

Jim had 57¢.   ¢

He spent 32¢.   —   ¢

Jim had this
   much left.   ¢

Pam had 14¢.   ¢

Jill had 35¢.   +   ¢

Pam and Jill
   had this much.   ¢

CHAPTER 6 CUMULATIVE REVIEW

Add.

$$
\begin{array}{r} 6\,3 \\ +1\,8 \\ \hline \end{array}
\qquad
\begin{array}{r} 3\,5 \\ +2\,7 \\ \hline \end{array}
\qquad
\begin{array}{r} 4\,6 \\ +3\,8 \\ \hline \end{array}
\qquad
\begin{array}{r} 5\,2 \\ +1\,9 \\ \hline \end{array}
\qquad
\begin{array}{r} 7\,4 \\ +1\,8 \\ \hline \end{array}
$$

$$
\begin{array}{r} 4\,8 \\ +2\,7 \\ \hline \end{array}
\qquad
\begin{array}{r} 5\,7 \\ +1\,7 \\ \hline \end{array}
\qquad
\begin{array}{r} 6\,5 \\ +2\,5 \\ \hline \end{array}
\qquad
\begin{array}{r} 2\,9 \\ +2\,4 \\ \hline \end{array}
\qquad
\begin{array}{r} 3\,7 \\ +4\,6 \\ \hline \end{array}
$$

$$
\begin{array}{r} 4\,3 \\ +1\,7 \\ \hline \end{array}
\qquad
\begin{array}{r} 1\,4 \\ +2\,7 \\ \hline \end{array}
\qquad
\begin{array}{r} 3\,5 \\ +\ 7 \\ \hline \end{array}
\qquad
\begin{array}{r} 2\,6 \\ +5\,5 \\ \hline \end{array}
\qquad
\begin{array}{r} 3\,8 \\ +2\,6 \\ \hline \end{array}
$$

$$
\begin{array}{r} 4\,2 \\ +1\,8 \\ \hline \end{array}
\qquad
\begin{array}{r} 5\,5 \\ +2\,5 \\ \hline \end{array}
\qquad
\begin{array}{r} 6\,8 \\ +1\,5 \\ \hline \end{array}
\qquad
\begin{array}{r} 3\,9 \\ +3\,8 \\ \hline \end{array}
\qquad
\begin{array}{r} 2\,7 \\ +4\,6 \\ \hline \end{array}
$$

Solve each problem.

Maria has 36 pennies.

Pablo has 52 pennies. $+$ _____

How many pennies in all?

Ann made 18 baskets.

Grant made 24 baskets. $+$ _____

How many baskets in all?

Subtract.

35 −16	26 − 9	43 −27	52 −18	60 −24

71 −23	84 −17	37 −29	95 −48	80 −36

85 −27	72 −49	91 −56	53 −15	44 − 9

66 −18	27 −18	48 −28	21 −14	32 −25

Solve each problem.

Micah had 42 marbles.

He gave away 18 marbles.

How many does he have left?

A box has 43 bottles and cans.

27 are bottles.

How many are cans?

CHAPTER 7   CUMULATIVE REVIEW

Write the numerals.

4 hundreds 3 tens 2 ones	6 hundreds 0 tens 7 ones
_____	_____
3 hundreds 1 ten 6 ones	5 hundreds 8 tens 1 one
_____	_____

Add.

$$\begin{array}{r} 5\,0\,0 \\ +2\,0\,0 \\ \hline \end{array} \qquad \begin{array}{r} 3\,0\,0 \\ +6\,0\,0 \\ \hline \end{array} \qquad \begin{array}{r} 4\,1\,2 \\ +2\,8\,7 \\ \hline \end{array} \qquad \begin{array}{r} 5\,0\,6 \\ +7\,1 \\ \hline \end{array}$$

$$\begin{array}{r} 7\,1\,5 \\ +1\,0\,2 \\ \hline \end{array} \qquad \begin{array}{r} 3\,9\,0 \\ +2\,0\,4 \\ \hline \end{array} \qquad \begin{array}{r} 2\,2\,2 \\ +3\,5 \\ \hline \end{array} \qquad \begin{array}{r} 4\,8\,0 \\ +3\,1\,7 \\ \hline \end{array}$$

Subtract.

$$\begin{array}{r} 7\,0\,0 \\ -2\,0\,0 \\ \hline \end{array} \qquad \begin{array}{r} 9\,0\,0 \\ -6\,0\,0 \\ \hline \end{array} \qquad \begin{array}{r} 8\,5\,6 \\ -5\,3\,2 \\ \hline \end{array} \qquad \begin{array}{r} 6\,9\,5 \\ -7\,3 \\ \hline \end{array}$$

$$\begin{array}{r} 5\,6\,8 \\ -1\,2 \\ \hline \end{array} \qquad \begin{array}{r} 4\,5\,9 \\ -2\,0\,7 \\ \hline \end{array} \qquad \begin{array}{r} 6\,8\,3 \\ -8\,1 \\ \hline \end{array} \qquad \begin{array}{r} 7\,1\,4 \\ -5\,1\,2 \\ \hline \end{array}$$